SHORT WAVE RADIO LISTENERS' HANDBOOK

SHORT WAVE RADIO LISTENERS' HANDBOOK

The complete guide to SWLing

Arthur Miller

Patrick Stephens
Wellingborough, Northamptonshire

First published in 1987

British Library Cataloguing in Publication Data

Miller, Arthur
   Short wave radio listeners' handbook.
   1. Radio, short wave—Receivers and
   reception—Amateurs' manuals
   I. Title
   621.3841'366   TK9945

   ISBN 0-85059-883-4

Patrick Stephens Limited is part of
Thorsons Publishing Group

Printed in Great Britain by Woolnough Bookbinding,
Irthlingborough, Northants

10 9 8 7 6 5 4 3 2 1

Contents

Acknowledgements

The author is pleased to acknowledge the assistance received from the following individuals and organizations during the compilation of this book: David A. Whitaker, BRS 25429 (who offered helpful advice and checked the manuscript); *World Radio TV Handbook* (especially Andrew Sennitt, editor, and Glenn Heffernan, publisher, of Billboard Publications Inc); Swiss Radio International; South Midlands Communications Ltd; Lowe Electronics Ltd; ICOM (UK) Ltd (formerly Thanet Electronics Ltd); Department of Trade and Industry.

Introduction

Short wave radio is certainly a remarkable hobby. It can be pursued twenty-four hours per day every day of the year, both indoors and outside the home and whatever the state of the weather. It is entertaining, educational and can be very exciting. It is not restricted to any age group and appeals to women as well as men. Unlike many other hobbies it need not involve considerable expenditure, though those who want to spend a fortune can do so!

With that kind of build-up it is perhaps surprising that short wave radio is not more popular than it is. It is not in the same league as gardening or fishing and has less devotees than, say, philately. Even so, the number of radio fans is increasing rapidly at the present time, due mainly to the impact of CB radio.

I have been a keen short wave radio listener for more than thirty years. During that time I have been aware of the undoubted fact that many people who become involved with radio lose their interest very quickly and have looked for reasons for this state of affairs.

There are, it seems, two main factors which explain the situation. Firstly, many people who become listeners are comparatively young — often still at school — and have many other interests and pressures to occupy their time. Unless they are reasonably successful at the outset they move on to other things. Secondly, and probably more importantly, basic information about short wave listening is not as readily available as it might be. There are several books dealing with the technical side of radio which sometimes aim to encourage readers to become radio amateurs, but these almost invariably assume that some background knowledge of the hobby has already been gained. Short wave listeners (or SWLs, as they are generally known) to the broadcast bands are catered for even more inadequately.

This book is dedicated to newcomers to short wave listening and people who would like to become involved but do not know where to start. At the same time I hope that more experienced listeners will be able to advance their knowledge of radio communications. It is not a technical manual and does not involve itself in such topics as radio circuitry, electrical formulae and the like, which can be studied from comprehensive reference works covering these subjects. Moreover, it does not deal, except in passing, with the more sophisticated aspects of amateur radio such as amateur television, radio teletype and communications satellites. What the book does aim to do is to explain the need for suitable equipment, describe the short wave radio frequency ranges and indicate the types of transmissions which may be heard and how to verify them. It also deals with contests and awards, since the hobby is often highly competitive.

It is of course axiomatic that there would be no listeners if there were no stations to hear — and vice versa! Broadcasting stations (such as the BBC, Voice of America, Radio Moscow, *etc.*) exist to provide their audiences with programmes which they hope the listeners will want to hear. They get their feedback in letters from listeners. Amateur radio, on the other hand, involves conversations between amateurs which may also be heard by listeners with suitable receivers; these listeners may then write to the stations if they so wish but they cannot talk to them 'over the air'. Not surprisingly, many SWLs find this unsatisfactory and endeavour to obtain qualifications to get a transmitting licence. A chapter on this subject is included in the book.

As for Citizens' Band radio (usually known as 'CB'), the position is somewhat different. Although it is possible to listen to CB stations without having the equipment to talk to them, the vast majority of CB operators have transceivers (combined transmitters and receivers) which enable them to have conversations with other CB enthusiasts. It is in fact unusual for people to listen to the CB stations as they would to amateur and broadcasting stations. Since this is a *listeners'* handbook it could be argued that the chapter dealing with CB radio is out of place. It has, however, been included because thousands of CB fans have turned their attentions to amateur radio as time has gone on and it is considered worthwhile to draw comparisons between the two interests.

Introduction to the short waves

The words 'short wave' conjure up a mystique which is not shared by long waves and medium waves. That is not to say that listening to the long and medium wavebands is uninteresting, for experts regularly get some exciting catches, but it does call for great skill and it is far better to graduate to these bands from the short waves rather than the other way round.

One of the reasons why short wave radio has gained its reputation is that it is virtually unknown to the so-called man-in-the-street in Great Britain. The BBC, until it started using VHF transmissions in stereo, transmitted its programmes for listeners in the UK only on long wave and medium wave and its domestic audience therefore had no need to investigate what the short waves had to offer. Its overseas audience, however, used to listen to the BBC World Service mainly on short wave.

Older readers will clearly recall the BBC Light Programme (now known as Radio 2) which used to be transmitted on 1500 metres/200 kilohertz long wave. This channel is still used by the present Radio 4. They may also remember the English language programmes of Radio Luxembourg on 1293 metres. The main feature of the long wave range (which may be defined as below 500 kilohertz/600 metres) is that it provides good, reliable signals over fairly short distances for stations which run high powers. There are some 'wide open spaces' on the dial as few stations can take advantage of the special attributes of long wave propagation unless they aim for a very small catchment area. Listeners in Britain will rarely hear stations beyond Western Europe.

Broadcast stations which wish to be heard beyond their country boundaries need to consider the medium wave or short wave ranges. On these frequencies they can operate with far less power and will be heard over much longer distances. Medium wave, which may be said to cover roughly from 500 kilohertz to 1600 kilohertz (185 to 600 metres), has many advantages in terms of economy but is not short of disadvantages either. Because the bands are so heavily populated, stations very often interfere with each other's transmissions, especially after dark, and fading of signals can be quite a problem. On the medium waves European listeners will receive a good selection of stations from their own and other European countries, but reception of stations from outside Europe can be quite a challenge.

It is on the short waves that long-distance reception really comes into its own. Unlike medium wave signals which use radio waves which travel close to the ground, short wave propagation uses the ionosphere to despatch signals all round the world and short waves may be defined as frequencies of 1600 kilohertz (kHz) upwards. Not only do broadcasting stations operate on short wave for international audiences, but one can also find on the short wave range radio amateurs and 'utility' stations operated by police, air traffic control, shipping and allied services. CB radio is also allocated to the short waves.

The terms 'wavelength' and 'frequency' are used to indicate the channels on which radio stations operate and these must be explained at the outset if confusion is to be avoided. Wavelengths are measured in metres and frequencies in kilohertz (kHz) or megahertz (MHz) per second. A megahertz is of course equivalent to 1000 kilohertz. (These terms were formerly expressed as megacycles and kilocycles, which had exactly the same meanings.) A wavelength of one metre corresponds to a frequency of 300,000 kilohertz or 300 MHz. As the frequency with which radio waves are produced increases, the length of the wave decreases, so it is a simple matter to convert the wavelength of a station to its frequency by using the formula:

$$\text{Wavelength (metres)} = \frac{300,000}{\text{Frequency (kHz)}}$$

Likewise, to convert frequency to wavelength, the formula is:

$$\text{Frequency (kHz)} = \frac{300,000}{\text{Wavelength (metres)}}$$

Frequency in MHz is generally given to three decimal places and wavelength in metres to two decimal places.

Most receivers are now calibrated in kilohertz but some older models intended for the casual listener rather than the enthusiast have dials which record the wavelengths only. Broadcasting stations very often announce their channels in both wavelengths and frequencies for the convenience of their listeners.

Let us now look at the types of stations which may be heard on the short wavebands. As the broadcasting stations use the majority of the spectrum it is convenient to start with them.

The terms 'broadcast stations', 'broadcasting stations' and 'BC stations' are synonymous. They refer to those stations which provide for their audience programmes of news, music, drama, comedy, propaganda, *etc*. Very often these stations are under the control of the governments of the countries in which they are located or they may be quasi-governmental agencies. Other stations, of which there are not a few, run on commercial lines and carry advertising. Some stations are controlled by religious organizations and funded by church authorities and/or donations.

The major BC stations broadcast in several languages but those whose main interest is to inform the local population will often confine themselves to the language or languages of the country where they are located. A knowledge of languages is undoubtedly a great help to the serious BC bands listener though stations often use musical identification signals from time to time as well as known verbal identifications.

The quality of programmes transmitted by broadcast stations ranges from the enlightened to the abysmal. Some manage to put together varied programmes with the right balance of news, views and music. On the other hand it can be very heavy going to sit through some of the political propaganda which is churned out incessantly by some stations. Even those listeners who may agree with the political views expressed are likely to lose interest after a while.

We tend to think of 'pirate' stations as dating from the mid-sixties with the boom in off-shore broadcasting stations such as Radio Caroline and Radio Veronica, and that may indeed have been the start of the pop music pirates. Long before this era, though, short wave radio was being used by unlicensed stations (known sometimes as 'clandestines') for political purposes. More often than not their stance was opposed to the government of the country where they claimed to be. Such stations can still be heard on the BC bands, very often being heavily jammed to prevent their messages being heard.

The main High Frequency broadcast bands are to be found on the following frequencies:

2300–2498 kHz (120 metres)	9500–9775 kHz (31 metres)
3200–3400 kHz (90 metres)	11700–11975 kHz (25 metres)
3900–4000 kHz (75 metres)	15100–15450 kHz (19 metres)
4750–5060 kHz (60 metres)	17700–17900 kHz (16 metres)
5950–6200 kHz (49 metres)	21450–21750 kHz (13 metres)
7100–7300 kHz (41 metres)	25600–26100 kHz (11 metres)

Unlike amateur stations, broadcast stations do not always keep to these recognized frequency ranges and it is normal to find stations operating between these ranges. For general listening, the most useful wavebands are 49, 41, 31, 25 and 19 metres; it is here that one finds the strongest stations and the most reliable propagation.

The short waves are also used by the one-and-a-half million radio amateurs licensed throughout the world. They are allocated frequency ranges and are not allowed to stray from them. Amateur radio is recognized in almost all countries of the world but political considerations sometimes intervene, and when countries are in turmoil the authorities often ban operation by amateur stations. Amateur radio is a remarkably reliable barometer of the world political situation.

The High Frequency allocations given to amateurs are as follows. Not all of these ranges are available in each country. Many countries do not have access to the 160 metres band and there are some restrictions on 80 metres.

1800–2000 kHz (160 metres)	18068–18168 kHz (16 metres)
3500–4000 kHz (80/75 metres)	21000–21450 kHz (15 metres)
7000–7300 kHz (40 metres)	24890–24990 kHz (12 metres)
10100–10150 kHz (30 metres)	28000–29700 kHz (10 metres)
14000–14350 kHz (20 metres)	

The segments 3800 to 4000 kHz and 7100 to 7300 kHz are not available to European amateurs though that does not of course stop listeners from monitoring them.

The 10, 18 and 24 MHz ranges are known colloquially as the 'WARC Bands', since they came into being as a result of the World Administrative Radio Conference in 1979. They are not as yet widely used and operation is normally restricted to the morse code.

Transmissions on the amateur bands enable amateur radio enthusiasts to contact each other and discuss matters of mutual interest. In addition to speech transmissions amateurs may also use the morse code (abbreviated to CW, for 'continuous wave'), radio teletype (RTTY), involving the use of teleprinters, and even television. Of course, special equipment needs to be used for the transmission and reception of RTTY and TV since a radio receiver alone does not have the facilities for resolving these signals.

Whilst the use of the morse code still remains popular it could be true that the majority of amateur contacts these days are made using plain speech. Amplitude Modulation (AM) has completely disappeared from the bands and almost all contacts are now made using Single Sideband (SSB), with a handful of stations using Frequency Modulation (FM) on the 28 MHz band. Both CW and SSB need to be resolved by a Beat Frequency Oscillator (BFO), and receivers which do not employ a BFO in their circuitry cannot be used for reception of amateur signals satisfactorily. In the absence of a BFO, SSB signals have been described as 'sounding like Donald Duck' — they can be readily heard but not understood.

Where SSB gains over the AM signals formerly transmitted by amateurs and still produced by the broadcasting stations is that it puts the power of the signal into a much smaller bandwidth, thereby giving it extra punch. An AM signal is comprised of a lower sideband, a carrier and an upper sideband with the carrier being equal in width to the width of the two sidebands. Using SSB therefore reduces the width of the signal to one-quarter of an AM signal, which also has the effect of providing space for more stations to transmit on today's crowded bands. To resolve the signal for reception purposes it is necessary to reintroduce the carrier and this is done by the receiver's BFO. There is no doubt that the advent of SSB has made an enormous impact on amateur radio and has made it far easier to log low-powered stations which would have been inaudible in the past.

One has to remember that the transmitter power of amateur stations is minute compared to that enjoyed by the broadcasters. Whereas a major BC station may use hundreds of kilowatts, few countries allow their amateurs to use more than one kilowatt, and powers of no higher than 150 watts are common. Some amateurs welcome the challenge of low power (QRP) and confine themselves to less than ten watts. A good antenna, or exceptional propagation conditions, is essential for contacts using such low power.

The amateur bands are divided into CW and telephony portions. The CW segments are to be found at the lower ends of the bands. On 14 MHz, for instance, morse is transmitted from 14000 to 14100 kHz with SSB from 14100 to 14350 kHz. On 21 MHz, the CW portion is from 21000 to 21150 kHz. One does occasionally hear stations in the 'wrong' portion of the band, but this is not common; it generally happens where, after talking to a station on the one mode, the operator then asks for a contact on the other mode.

Amateur stations have to be licensed by the appropriate authorities in their countries and have to satisfy the powers-that-be that they are competent people to operate radio stations. To obtain a full licence the would-be amateur normally has to pass a technical examination, including questions about the licensing conditions, and a morse test. Most countries also issue licences to persons who wish to operate only on the VHF bands and the morse test is generally dispensed with in these cases. Some countries, such as the USA, have several classes of licence with different conditions attaching to each. The regulations which apply in the United Kingdom are described in a later chapter.

It must be stressed that only persons who have obtained transmitting licences are allowed to transmit on the amateur bands. Short wave listeners do not have to obtain licences and, although they are subject to certain other restrictions, they are free to listen to amateur stations in the same way that they can listen to broadcasting stations. Many people, unfamiliar with the hobby, question whether this is ethical. Are they not merely eavesdropping on other people's conversations? Well, yes and no...

Amateurs are fully aware when they go on the air that other people are listening to them. It is only because people hear them that they are able to make contacts (or QSOs). Their discussions are not such that they want to keep them private. And they know that today's listener may well be tomorrow's amateur. After all, they almost certainly started as listeners themselves. Far from being annoyed that their conversations are being heard by listeners who cannot speak to them directly, almost all amateurs welcome the interest shown by the listening fraternity.

Before moving on it might be as well to clear up that old chestnut, the 'amateurs *v.* hams' controversy. The official name of the hobby is amateur radio and its participants are known as radio amateurs. Since so many things have become abbreviated over the years it is not surprising that the word 'amateur' soon dropped its last two syllables and added an 'h' in front of the remaining syllable because it sounded better that way. Thus 'amateurs' became 'hams' and the hobby became 'ham radio'. Many English-speaking amateurs dislike this development and one can hardly blame them. The word 'ham' implies incompetence, as in the expression 'a ham actor', and amateurs as a whole are far from being that. Quite the reverse in fact, for amateurs have been instrumental in advancing not only amateur radio but also radio in general from the dawn of radio communications. Surprisingly, perhaps, our North American friends are less sensitive over the appellation and 'ham radio' is more readily accepted on that side of the Atlantic. Perhaps they don't have ham actors over there!

Citizens' Band radio, or 'CB' as it is generally known, is also to be found on the short wavebands in the 27 MHz (11 metres) range. Since this hobby is also enjoyed by people who are not professional broadcasters it is sometimes confused with amateur radio. There are nevertheless significant differences which will be more fully explained in the chapter on Citizens' Band radio. The most obvious difference to those who listen to both amateurs and CB is that the latter is far more informal; many of the participants know each other personally and this is clearly reflected in their conversations.

Although CB has several uses it is best known for its social aspects. Friends use it to exchange news as they would the telephone — and often at cheaper cost! A casual eavesdropper on the CB band could well be embarrassed by the nature of some of the discussions. A more serious use of the waveband is the exchange of information about traffic conditions, *etc.*, since very many operators have CB transceivers in their cars and lorries and can communicate with each other when there are traffic delays or diversions. It is also a means by which employees of companies can keep in touch with their head offices. Because of the low powers used the range of transmissions is very small — generally only a few miles — unless there are very good propagation conditions when intercontinental contacts are possible.

CB stations can be heard using AM, FM and SSB modes, which can all be copied on a typical communications receiver. In the UK the only legal mode is FM (Frequency Modulation), though some stations still retain the AM equipment which they acquired before the hobby was legally authorized. A CB radio licence is required for both transmission on the CB band *and* reception of the stations.

The name 'utilities' will ring a bell with Monopoly players. This title relates to stations operated by public service authorities such as airports, police, *etc.* Most of these services now operate on VHF but some can still be found on the lower frequencies. In the UK it is illegal to listen to their transmissions, contrary to the widely held view that one can listen to them providing one does not disclose information about what is heard. This confusion probably arises because listeners will often hear 'utility' stations whilst they are searching for stations which they are legally allowed to hear; indeed, at times (as on 160 metres) they can hardly miss them. In these circumstances they are prohibited from divulging any information which they may unwittingly receive.

British legislation in this respect is far more restrictive than in almost all other countries. There is no doubt a strong case for taking this line with police transmissions, but it is hard to justify in other instances. The official view is that these stations are not 'broadcasting stations' within the meaning of the Wireless Telegraphy Act 1949 and they therefore fall outside the range of stations which may be heard.

The biggest nonsense of all is that concerning the so-called time signal stations. These are stations which operate in several countries to provide highly accurate time checks and information about propagation conditions. Since they transmit on standard frequencies, which are often an exact multiple of one megahertz, they are very useful for checking the calibration of one's receiver. The broadcasts are intended to be of benefit to anyone involved with short wave radio whether in a professional or an enthusiast capacity and the stations often welcome reception reports from listeners which they will happily verify. Yet in the UK, listeners are not officially allowed to listen to these most useful transmissions (although licensed radio amateurs can!).

In times of poor propagation conditions it is sometimes possible to hear amateur stations using satellites. The amateur radio service has in fact constructed its own communications satellites, known as 'OSCARS', which circle the earth and allow two-way communications between amateurs in conditions where normal ionospheric contacts would be impossible. The satellites use the 28 MHz band on a limited range of frequencies and signals bounced off them can be heard for a few minutes every couple of hours. In that way it is sometimes possible for European amateurs to talk to their counterparts in the United States but each contact has to be very brief and is generally restricted to an exchange of signal report.

We now need to consider the meanings of the abbreviations LF, HF, VHF and UHF. Short wave radio is divided into various frequency ranges. Those frequencies between 1.8 and 30 MHz are known as the High Frequencies (HF) though, confusingly, the range between 1.8 and 7 MHz may also be known as the Low Frequencies (LF) to indicate the lower frequencies included in the HF range! The VHF (Very High Frequency) bands extend from 30 to 300 MHz and any frequencies above 300 MHz are known as UHF (Ultra High Frequencies).

It is not just a question of semantics. We have already seen that the characteristics of the long and medium wavebands are quite different from those of the short wavebands below 30 MHz, and it is equally the case that the characteristics of the bands above 30 MHz are totally different from those of the HF bands. For this reason we devote a complete chapter to the VHF bands in an effort to minimize the confusion.

The VHF broadcast bands run from 66 to 72 MHz in Eastern Europe and 87 to 108 MHz elsewhere. In normal circumstances reception is confined to stations within a small radius of the listener's home such as the BBC national and local stations and the commercial stations authorised by the IBA. During propagation disturbances, however, it is sometimes possible to hear stations in Western Europe.

There is plenty of activity from amateurs on the 144 to 146 MHz (2 metres) band. Many newly licensed stations begin on this band with licences which do not permit them to operate on the HF bands. The police are also regular users of VHF and can often be heard on the same range as the BC stations. The amateur bands of 70 MHz (4 metres) and 430 to 440 MHz (70 centimetres) come into prominence during contests or when conditions are exceptionally good but listeners may have to wait weeks between hearing stations in normal circumstances. SWLs in densely populated areas are likely to be the most successful on these two bands because of the higher level of activity there.

Another amateur band in the VHF range is that covering 50 to 54 MHz (6 metres). This has long been used in North America and became available on an experimental basis in Great Britain very recently, though few other European countries presently occupy it.

Communication on the HF bands makes use of the ionosphere to project signals over considerable distances and this is where 1.8 to 30 MHz differs from the other short wave frequencies. Ionized regions exist in the upper atmosphere and reflect signals which come into contact with them. As the height and density of the ionosphere varies considerably, influenced by the effects of the sun, propagation conditions vary from day to day and from hour to hour and they provide the unpredictability which is not a feature of long wave and medium wave propagation and which makes short wave listening so fascinating. That is not to say that short wave propagation is entirely unpredictable all of the time, but one certainly cannot guarantee to hear the same station at the same time every day of the week even if it is known to transmit to a regular schedule.

Sunspots play a most important part in communications on the HF bands. These are not holiday resorts, as has been jokingly suggested, but are described in the Oxford Illustrated Dictionary as 'cavities in photosphere appearing as dark spots or patches on sun's surface, lasting from a few hours to several months, recurring in greatest numbers at intervals of a little over eleven years, and frequently accompanied by magnetic disturbances *etc.* on earth'. Without these sunspots our hobby would be far less interesting.

Increases in the number of sunspots lead to increased ionization of the atmosphere and result in improvements in reception conditions. The very best conditions are to be found at 'sunspot maximum' and the comparison between then and 'sunspot minimum' is so great as to be almost unbelievable. During the minimum of the eleven-year cycle it is not unusual for months to go by without any sunspot activity at all. Sunspots have been observed by scientists for three or four centuries but they are still not fully understood. Nowadays there are daily sunspot counts which show the increase or decline in their numbers and provide a guide to likely reception conditions. The most recent maxima occurred in 1947, 1958, 1969 and 1980; the next will arrive around 1991. The number of sunspots occurring at the cycle peak is far from uniform and the reception conditions experienced at one sunspot maximum can be noticeably different from those at the peak of another cycle. It is generally accepted that the 1947 sunspot maximum provided the best radio conditions ever experienced and it is widely believed that its like will not be seen again during the lifetime of most, if not all, of us.

One of the main effects of the sunspot maximum is that it enables stations to use higher frequencies than would otherwise be the case on a regular basis. To take the amateur bands as an example, during the sunspot maximum and for the couple of years preceding and following it one can hear stations on 28 MHz (10 metres) every day with exceptionally strong signals regardless of distance. Similar conditions are experienced on 21 MHz (15 metres). Come the sunspot minimum, though, and one may listen for a month or two without hearing a single station on 10 metres (apart from stations near to one's home), and it will be a struggle to hear anything worthwhile on 15 metres on many occasions. The highest frequency which can be satisfactorily used for transmission is known as the Maximum Usable Frequency (MUF).

Fortunately the conditions on the lower frequencies below, say, 10 MHz improve as the higher frequencies decline and many listeners use the opportunity to hear new countries on these lower bands. Of course, there is more activity on the lower bands at these times since stations are unable to use the higher bands and have to look for alternative channels. This is true not only of amateurs but also of the broadcasting stations as well.

The effects of the sunspot cycle are clearly shown in the accompanying graphs covering the period 1975 to 1985 inclusive. These show the number of countries I have heard on SSB on each amateur band from 3.5 to 28 MHz in each year. They do not of course show all of the countries which could have been heard had more listening been done but they do show very distinctly the

Graph of countries heard on 3.5 and 7 MHz SSB from 1975 to 1985.

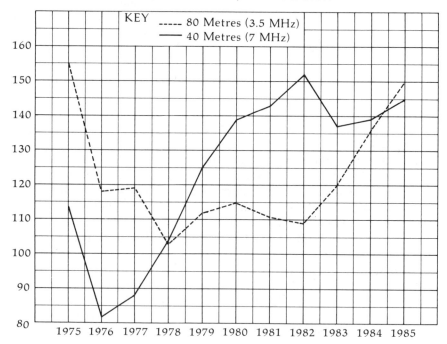

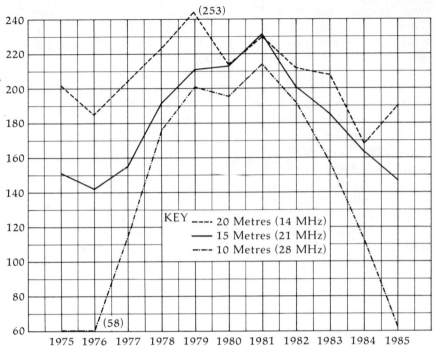

Graph of countries heard on 14, 21 and 28 MHz SSB from 1975 to 1985.

variations in conditions from year to year and correspond fairly closely with the results achieved by other SWLs who have been consulted. Note particularly that fifty-eight countries were heard on 10 metres in 1976 (many of which would have been European) compared with 213 in 1981. That tells its own story!

Because it is generally known that the sun has an effect on short wave radio propagation, it is a common misconception that there is a strong connection between radio conditions and the weather (WX). In other words, if the sun is shining the reception will be good. This is a fallacy insofar as HF bands are concerned: the state of the weather is quite immaterial. On VHF it can be a different story, as we shall see later.

Unlike local broadcasting stations which can be heard at the same signal strength regardless of the time of day, short wave reception is susceptible to fading (QSB) which can and does cause extreme problems for listeners. If there is no other station transmitting nearby one may well be able to copy the desired station despite the fading, but in other circumstances the transmissions will be lost altogether. Fading may be slow or rapid depending on the conditions. Sometimes stations have signals with a fluttery sound which appears as very fast fading but which may well indicate that the station's signals are being transmitted over the North Pole. It could also indicate that the signals are being subjected to the effects of the aurora borealis. Fluttery sounding signals are worthy of the very closest attention, for they may well signify unusual conditions which will benefit the listener greatly.

QSB can be a nuisance but it could have interesting side-effects. When it comes to QRM (electrical interference) nothing good can be advanced in its favour. It is without doubt the biggest headache facing the short wave enthusiast; those who cannot afford to turn to drink may give up the hobby altogether!

Interference comes in many forms and, sadly, some of them are quite deliberate. Listeners differentiate between atmospheric interference, which is known by the abbreviation QRN, and all other forms, which are designated QRM. QRN is experienced as static crashes and generally occurs during thunderstorms or in summer weather. It can be quite severe, especially on the lower frequencies. QRM includes such things as interference from electrical appliances (including television sets, hi-fi radios and record players, home computers and vacuum cleaners), more than one station transmitting on the same channel, and deliberate jamming of transmissions.

There is little that can be done about some of these forms of QRM. Television sets radiate a form of QRM known as 'television timebase' which appears as a form of buzzing noise every 25 kHz or so across the dial; it can be more prevalent on the lower frequencies and will often prevent reception of the weakest stations. Although it is likely to be worse if the offending set is in one's own home, it can emanate from TV sets used by neighbours in the immediate vicinity. Fluorescent lights are also a considerable problem as they cause a constant noise which affects all frequencies; it is advisable not to use fluorescent lights in one's own house if possible. Vacuum cleaners are less of a problem since they are used only intermittently, but they may obliterate all reception when they are in use. In winter, central heating systems can be a problem, especially when the pumps are brought into play, but some systems are interference-free. Power lines can cause serious problems, particularly in wet weather. Some receivers have filters which can reduce the problems of interference but they generally reduce the volume of stations being heard as well.

A source of QRM which invariably baffles newcomers takes the form of a loud, rapid hammering sound covering a wide range of frequencies and lasting for two or three minutes at a time followed by a very short break. Those who have heard this QRM know it by its nickname of 'the woodpecker', for fairly obvious reasons. This noise comes from a Soviet radar station in the Ukraine and is a tremendous nuisance. (At the time of writing it is far less prevalent than it used to be.)

QRM caused by one station to another is often the result of too many stations trying to operate in too restricted a space. Amateurs can sometimes help themselves by moving to another frequency but this is not possible with BC stations which transmit to fixed schedules. Where reception conditions are good there is more likely to be trouble from weaker stations which would not normally be audible over long distances. Broadcasting stations welcome information about QRM sources and use this to plan their future schedules.

Deliberate QRM has long been a source of anger for serious listeners. It happens on both the broadcasting and the amateur bands but is most pronounced on the former. When one tunes across the BC bands and hears tremendously loud noise covering several kilohertz at a time, one can be certain that underneath the racket is a station which someone does not want to be heard. Most of this type of QRM is due to attempts, almost always successful, to obliterate stations which certain governments find embarrassing to them. Because the operation is such an overkill it has the effect of drowning out other stations which may broadcast completely uncontroversial material and which give offence to no-one.

Amateur radio is generally conducted in a more cordial manner but is not entirely free of silly people who take delight in making things unpleasant for others. Their efforts usually involve whistling, making scratching and rustling noises and talking whilst other stations are in contact. Since they obviously do not identify themselves there is no certainty that they *are* amateurs themselves; they could be total imposters. Fortunately there are very few of these people around and they are only really a problem at present on the upper portion of the 80 metres band.

Having read this far, readers will have realized that abbreviations play their part in short wave radio. Already we have noted such terms as QRM, QRN, QSB, MUF, SWL and WX. Most abbreviations are confined to the amateur bands but some have wider applications. A person's home, for instance, is his QTH; a card verifying reception is a QSL card; a receiver is an RX and a transmitter a TX; the QSA-R code is a means of describing the readability and strength of an amateur signal and the BC equivalent is the SINPO code. Many of these abbreviations will be explained in more detail elsewhere in this book, and the appendices give a list of the more common terms and abbreviations used in short wave radio.

The abbreviation which causes much excitement is 'DX' (one of several ending in the letter 'X'). DX used to signify distance and a DX station was therefore one located at a considerable distance from the listener's location. As science progressed over the years it became relatively easy to hear some distant countries and the most desirable catches then became stations from rare locations. As an example, one could hear Australia fairly regularly because there were many stations operating from there, but there may have been only one station in Kuwait which was on the air for twenty minutes every Tuesday afternoon. Given this scenario, the Kuwaiti station was much more awkward to hear in Europe even though it was much closer geographically. In time, therefore, the term 'DX' came to mean rare catches rather than any stations from a long distance, though the latter meaning has not been completely abandoned.

In this chapter I have endeavoured to give a general outline of short wave radio and the short wave listening hobby. Many of the topics touched upon will be covered in more detail later in the book.

Success as a short wave listener depends to some extent on being able to obtain current information about active stations. Broadcast stations do sometimes transmit DX bulletins which provide news about the BC bands. Other information can be obtained from club bulletins. Monthly magazines on sale in newsagents often contain limited information about the amateur and broadcast bands but mostly consist of technical articles which may not be of much interest to SWLs who merely want to listen to the stations. Moreover, the information included is often rather dated by the time it appears in print. Listeners may find it more advantageous to become members of specialist radio clubs which have their own magazines.

The Radio Society of Great Britain (RSGB) is the national amateur radio society to which many British amateurs belong. The Society publishes a monthly magazine called *Radio Communication* (often known as 'Radcom'), which deals with amateur radio topics but does not cover the BC bands. Listeners are admitted to membership on the same terms as radio amateurs and are entitled to use the same facilities including the QSL Bureau (see the chapter on Verifications). For details of membership the address to contact is: The New Member Department, Radio Society of Great Britian, Lambda House, Cranborne Road, Potters Bar, Hertfordshire, EN6 3JW.

The Society also publishes an excellent weekly bulletin, the DX News Sheet, which gives current information about activity on the amateur bands. This publication is highly recommended to all keen DXers. Subscribers do not have to be members of the RSGB.

The World DX Club (WDXC) has members in the United Kingdom and Europe as well as in the USA. This club caters for the broadcast bands enthusiasts and publishes an informative forty-page monthly bulletin entitled *Contact*. Well-known names in the world of BC radio are to be found in the membership lists of this organization, which was founded in 1968. For details of membership, write to 17 Motspur Drive, Northampton, NN2 6LY.

Other organizations which publish bulletins and which are worth investigating include: British DX Club (BDXC-UK), 54 Birkhall Road, Catford, London, SE6 1TE; DX Association of Great Britain (DXAGB), 35 Borough Avenue, Wallingford, Oxon, OX10 0TB; and International Listeners' Association, 1 Jersey Street, Hafod, Swansea, SA1 2HF.

Throughout the UK there are many local radio clubs and societies which welcome new members. Many of these clubs are devoted to amateur radio only and are affiliated to the RSGB. Details may be obtained from local newspaper reports or from RSGB HQ.

Receivers and Antennas

A jocular remark which one sometimes hears is that a station's signals are so strong that they can be heard without a receiver. This seemingly impossible feat has even been demonstrated. House-holders living in the immediate vicinity of very powerful broad-casting stations occasionally report that they can pick up radio programmes from their electric cookers or even the domestic water pipes! Such an occurrence always provides a good story for the local papers but it must be rather unnerving for the people involved. Moreover, it could be irritating for housewives who would prefer The Archers to pop music, since electric cookers do not have the means to change stations.

Of course, this type of thing is extremely rare and the rest of us will need to employ more conventional means to fill our logbooks. What we require is a suitable receiver and an aerial, the latter generally referred to as an antenna (ANT). Many listeners find that they can get good reception with a modest antenna, but the choice of receiver is rather more critical. We will firstly consider the choice of receiver (or RX, to use the standard abbreviation).

Receivers

The two main requirements of a receiver both begin with the letter 'S', namely Sensitivity and Selectivity. After being picked up by the antenna, the signals are converted by the receiver into a form which enables us to listen to them. The antenna will attract both strong and weak signals and the receiver has to sort them out for us. If the RX is not very sensitive the weaker signals will tend to get lost and we will probably miss the most interesting stations. However, if the RX does pull in the stations capably it then needs to be able to separate them so that we are able to hear them all, and this is where the selectivity comes into play.

Over the past few years enormous progress has been made in the field of electronics and, in real terms, a good receiver is much less expensive now than it was until comparatively recently. Whilst it is best to avoid the cheapest equipment on the market one certainly does not have to spend a considerable sum of money to get something very worthwhile, especially if one is purchasing second-hand.

Many of the cheaper receivers available today are designed to enable their owners to listen only to local stations. They frequently allow reception of only the long and medium wave ranges though some also cover the VHF broadcasting band. They usually have their own built-in antenna. Most of these sets are neither sensitive nor selective to an acceptable degree and cannot be recommended even to those whose only interest is the VHF bands.

The type of RX which is most suitable for short wave radio enthusiasts is known as a communications receiver. This contains many features which are not found on 'domestic' receivers and which are virtually essential for serious listening. Most communications receivers do not cover the VHF bands but allow for the addition of separate converters which can be bought as add-on units. As VHF is a specialist subject we will deal with VHF equipment, including antennas, in a later chapter, The VHF and UHF bands.

Some communications receivers are designed for the amateur bands only but will allow reception of some broadcasting stations which transmit on the same frequencies or close to the amateur bands. Other receivers, which are known as 'general coverage', include the entire frequency range over several megahertz and typically cover 0.5 MHz to 30.0 MHz, which allows reception of medium wave stations as well as short wave stations below the VHF bands. This is the type of receiver required by broadcast bands enthusiasts.

Whereas receivers once used to be very bulky and not always attractive in appearance, present-day equipment utilizes modern technology to great advantage. Sets can be moved around easily and do not look obtrusive in the family living room. Appearance isn't always a guide to performance but equipment marketed by the major manufacturers can usually be relied on to be of good standard.

What features should we look for when we contemplate buying a receiver? Firstly, we need to consider the use to which the RX will be put. If one's sole interest is in the amateur bands there is obviously a strong case for buying an RX which covers only the amateur frequencies, but that is rather more easily said than done. The present trend is towards manufacture of transceivers, or combined transmitters and receivers, and it is clearly a waste of money for a listener to buy such an item when he is not allowed to use the transmitter without a licence. These transceivers can be very expensive and should only be considered by listeners who expect to qualify as radio amateurs in due course. There are, however, some amateur-bands-only receivers which can be obtained on the second-hand market and these are well worthy of serious investigation. They are not in plentiful supply, unfortunately, for those people who have them tend to keep them since they cannot easily be replaced with new, similar models.

As we saw in the last chapter, the major amateur bands are 1.8 MHz (160 metres, sometimes called Top Band), 3.5 MHz (80 metres), 7 MHz (40 metres), 14 MHz (20 metres), 21 MHz (15 metres) and 28 MHz (10 metres). Some very old receivers do not cover 21 and 28 MHz, but it is doubtful if such models can be found today other than in a museum. 160 metres can be more of a problem since some models manufactured as recently as the seventies did not include this particular band. Use of 160 metres is restricted to certain countries but the list of countries has increased considerably during the past few years and there is now a great deal of interest in Top Band. When buying an RX it is worth checking that it does cover 160 metres or that it can be converted to do so, since it would be a pity not to be able to enjoy what is becoming a very interesting band. There does not at present seem to be very much activity on the so-called 'WARC Bands', and one has to be able to read the morse code to take advantage of what there is. Amateur bands receivers do not generally cover the 10 MHz, 18 MHz and 24 MHz bands and, ironically, one often needs a general coverage RX to listen to them.

Whilst receivers which cover only the broadcast bands are not unknown, they are very difficult to acquire. Those SWLs who want to monitor the BC bands will normally have to buy a general coverage RX which will also afford the opportunity of reception of the amateur bands. It is true – regrettably in my opinion – that most listeners eventually concentrate exclusively on either the amateur or the broadcast bands, but there is no valid reason why this should be. Both sides of the hobby have a great deal to offer and it can be very rewarding to listen to both types of communication. General coverage receivers also allow listeners to tune in to 'utility' stations, but there are legal restrictions to consider, as already explained.

There is an interesting selection of new general coverage receivers available (albeit at fairly high cost in some cases) and also a reasonable second-hand market, so there is no shortage of choice.

Although listeners are likely to operate from their homes for much of the time it is very pleasant to take advantage of what little good weather we have in this country to do some listening out of doors. Portable radios which operate from batteries are ideal for this purpose and one can also get receivers which can be powered by the mains or by batteries, including car batteries. Anyone wishing to do some SWLing in these circumstances should consider buying an RX which will operate from different power sources. Many of us are plagued by electrical interference and other hazards whilst at home and operating a receiver way out in the country can be a very enjoyable interlude. Providing that one does not trespass on property one can erect an antenna on a tree or similar and get some very worthwhile results. I once logged five continents in as many minutes whilst 'on safari' in the Cotswolds!

There is an old saying that 'you get what you pay for', but this needs to be treated with caution with regard to radio receivers. Citroën Cars ran an advert some time ago proclaiming that their 2CV cars costing £3,000 had many of the same features as cars costing twenty times as much, such as four wheels, an engine, *etc*! Similarly with radio equipment, it is often the 'luxuries' which boost the price enormously and these items can often be dispensed with without being sorely missed. In fact, it is sometimes said that they are little more than gimmicks anyway.

So what do we need? These are the questions we should be asking when looking for a receiver:

(a) Does it cover the frequency ranges on which we want to listen?

(b) If we want to listen out of doors or without a mains power supply, can it be operated from batteries?

(c) Can it be described as both sensitive and selective?

(d) Is the tuning sufficiently fine to enable us to separate the stations adequately?

(e) If we want to listen to amateur stations operating on SSB and CW, is there a Beat Frequency Oscillator (BFO)?

(f) Are there filters to enable us to reduce the level of interference?

(g) Is there a means of tuning the antenna?

(h) Is it comfortable to operate over long periods?

(i)   Is the calibration of the dial sufficiently accurate?

(j)   Does the loudspeaker provide reception of an adequate quality?

(k)   If the RX is an older model, can it be properly repaired if it breaks down?

(l)   Can it be operated with headphones if required?

(m) Can the signal strength of the stations heard be determined?
This list is not exhaustive but is given as a general guide.

Let us now look at some of these features in greater detail. The answers to some of the questions will be found in the manufacturers' literature, often in such technical detail that it may be incomprehensible to the layman. Where this is the case it is always worth asking for an interpretation from the salesman and requesting the opportunity of trying out the equipment for oneself.

It is particularly important that one should be able to determine the frequency at which the RX is operating to a high degree of accuracy. The ideal for listening purposes is to read the frequency to the nearest kilohertz. This is often possible with amateur bands receivers but is not so common with the general coverage types. Older RXs are less likely to have this ability than more recent models. Whilst the need to read the frequency accurately is slightly less important in broadcast bands listening than in amateur listening, an RX which cannot indicate the QRG to within ten kilohertz could cause a few problems.

The reasons for this are not difficult to appreciate. Broadcasting stations transmit on known frequencies and at scheduled times and it is convenient to be able to determine the QRG on the receiver precisely. The short wave radio spectrum is very crowded and it is quite usual for several stations to be allocated to the same channel. This can cause difficulties when one actually *finds* the channel but is obviously even worse if the listener can only estimate where he is tuning on the dial. It will not be too difficult to locate a powerful station if one is reasonably close to the QRG but it could well be impossible to identify a weaker one. For the most part, amateur stations do not operate to set schedules unless they are in regular contact with the same amateurs at pre-arranged intervals. They do not have any official right to occupy a particular channel and will have to move from the scheduled frequency if it proves unsuitable. If it is known that an amateur whom one wants to hear is to transmit at a certain time and 'place on the dial', one really needs to go directly to that QRG to have a good chance of finding him. On a busy band an error of just a couple of kilohertz could be critical.

Present-day receivers provide a read-out of the operating frequency either from a dial or from a digital display. Sets containing the latter facility are generally significantly more costly. They will normally indicate the QRG to one-tenth of a kilohertz (100 hertz) and that can often be very useful. Amateur stations sometimes announce that they are going to move frequency and will be going to, say, 3790.5 kHz. An RX without a digital read-out may be able to determine the channel to the nearest 500 hertz and it is not normally worth insisting on anything more precise than that. After all, it is only in recent times that one has been able to be so accurate on receivers available for non-professional use.

Where receivers do not have a frequency read-out, as with most older models, it is still possible to determine QRGs within acceptable tolerances, especially on the broadcast bands, by the use of graph paper. These receivers will normally show the frequency to the nearest megahertz and have a logging scale, probably with 100 graduations. If one takes the 15 MHz broadcast band, for instance, one needs to set the main indicator on the 15 MHz point on the dial and then use the logging pointer to note the QRGs of one station at the bottom end of the waveband and one station at the top end. Since international broadcasters who use this band sometimes have more than one channel, it is important to ensure that one identifies the correct channel by listening for station announcements. If a station on 15.110 MHz is found at point 20 on the logging scale and one on 15,410 MHz is at point 80 it is a simple matter to draw a graph which will identify the frequency of a station between those two points, as in the diagram. This same method can be used for all bands regularly used by the listener.

Virtually all communications receivers will have a Beat Frequency Oscillator (BFO) which allows for the reception of CW and SSB stations. It may not be shown as such on the front panel of the RX; most equipment of recent manufacture will have a Mode selection switch for reception of AM signals, Lower Sideband signals (LSB) and Upper Sideband and CW signals (USB-CW). There may also be a position on the control for AM reception with an automatic noise limiter (AM-ANL).

Interference is one of the most serious hazards facing listeners and there is no easy answer to it. It is one of the crosses we have to bear. There are many sources of interference and the best we can do is to try and reduce the nuisance since there is no way of eliminating

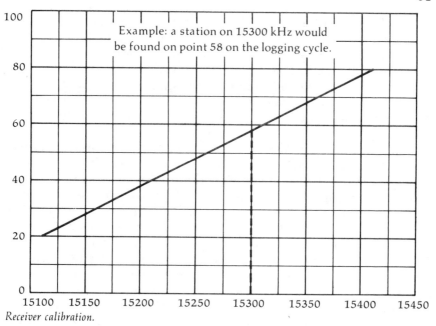

Example: a station on 15300 kHz would be found on point 58 on the logging cycle.

Receiver calibration.

it altogether. Receivers are sometimes provided with a variety of controls which allow reduction of the noise but which often also reduce the volume of the station signal substantially. An attenuator which cuts down the strength of very strong stations to give the weaker ones a chance of being heard is a good feature provided that one does not expect miracles from it. Even better, perhaps, is a series of filters which restrict the bandwidth of the channel being monitored; these are normally found only on the most expensive RXs but can sometimes be added as an optional extra. They are particularly useful on the lower frequencies, especially on the 40 metres amateur band. They can have a marked effect on the audio quality of the signal and are not recommended for listeners wanting to hear classical music!

A factor which is often forgotten by buyers of radio receivers (and, it seems, sometimes by manufacturers) is that listeners may want to monitor the short wavebands continuously over a long period of time. This happens especially where the SWL is taking part in a listening contest which may last for 24 or 48 hours. In an amateur radio contest the listener will have his hand on the tuning dial for several hours in total and if it is uncomfortable for him to operate he may well end up with a painful wrist which will trouble him for a few days afterwards. With the current vogue for miniaturization the size of RXs has become as small as it can be consistent with comfortable operating. Before buying an RX prospective purchasers who are thinking of intensive usage in contests or the like should consider whether the set they have in mind will allow them to operate in a relaxed manner. In particular the size of the tuning dial needs to be taken into account.

Amateur radio fans are not normally looking for hi-fi reception of stations and broadcast bands listeners will not usually get it. That, though, is no reason for ignoring the quality of reception via the receiver's loudspeaker. BC stations often transmit musical programmes, some of which are well worth hearing, and there is much to be said for having a speaker which performs competently. Some RXs have a built-in loudspeaker whereas others need an external speaker usually made by the same manufacturer and of similar appearance to the RX itself. Although the external speakers are often bigger they do not necessarily improve on the quality of reception and there is no strong reason for preferring them to built-in speakers. For reception of the weakest signals, or where the sound from the RX could be a nuisance to other members of the household, it is a good policy to use headphones. Indeed, it is amazing what a difference these can make and they may allow reception of some stations which are totally unintelligible on a loudspeaker. Some people use them all the time and this can be quite a useful policy if one's headphones are comfortable to wear. Receivers almost always have a socket to allow the use of headphones and it is advisable to read the manufacturer's handbook which will probably indicate the type of headphones which are recommended for the particular RX.

Most receivers constructed in the last twenty years have a facility for measuring the signal strength of stations being heard. This, hardly surprisingly, is known as an S-meter and is calibrated from SØ to S9 in stages of one S-point and then to S9 + 40dB or S9 + 60dB (+dB = decibels over S9). Theoretically this enables comparisons to be made between the strengths of the stations, but it needs to be used with care where more than one station is on the channel or there are stations on adjacent channels since the meter will register the strength of the strongest station being received. In practice, most listeners and not a few amateurs often ignore the S-meter completely and base their reports on their own estimates of the strengths of the stations being heard. In any event there is little point in using a meter report in isolation, though it can be useful for comparison purposes. In my opinion the absence of an S-meter should not be seen as a serious criticism of a receiver.

Another feature which is sometimes found on modern receivers, and usually adds noticeably to the cost, is a means of pre-setting frequencies so that they may be selected at the touch of a button. This device has of course long been found on car radios to save the car driver the bother of tuning around the dial when his hands would more safely be employed on the steering wheel. BC bands listeners might find such a system worthwhile if they regularly listen to the same stations, but it is not a lot of benefit to amateur bands listeners, for whom the extra cost of RXs with pre-selection facilities is rarely justified.

When considering receivers generally there is one point which cannot be too strongly emphasized: there is no substitute for experience! Just as a person buying the same type of camera as a leading photographer is unlikely initially to produce the same quality of pictures (if ever), so the ownership of a very expensive short wave receiver is no guarantee of success as a listener. Paradoxically, the opposite may even be true. One needs to be able to understand all the controls fully to get the best out of one's purchase and a beginner to the hobby may find that relatively simple equipment, which can be readily understood, is a better bet than de luxe equipment which needs experience to be utilized fully.

Most of the new receivers available nowadays are of Japanese manufacture — and very good they are too! However, it is not so long ago that Great Britain and the USA were building some of the finest equipment in the world and some examples of this can still be found on the second-hand market. It is worthwhile considering purchasing an older British or American RX in preference to a new receiver since some bargains can be obtained, but one needs to proceed with caution. These older sets use thermionic valves rather than transistors and microchips and such valves or suitable equivalents may not be obtainable today. If in doubt it might be as well to consult the manufacturers or to ask another enthusiast with a good technical knowledge of the hobby.

Receivers manufactured by Racal, such as the RA17 and RA71, and top-of-the-range Eddystone models such as the 750, EA-12 and the rarely seen 880, are generally considered the ultimate in British receiver design. When new they were so costly that only the most wealthy enthusiasts could buy them and most were sold to professional broadcasting stations such as the BBC. Eddystone produced a whole range of RXs for hobby use over a couple of decades after the Second World War and probably had the lion's share of the market for new equipment at a time when 'Army surplus' stock was favoured by listeners for its modest cost and — yes! — some people were still building their own receivers. Racal and Eddystone receivers are worth considering seriously as second-hand purchases. Of the American equipment, that manufactured by Collins and Drake has an excellent reputation but is not easily obtained this side of the Atlantic. Of course, receivers by other manufacturers can be found on the second-hand market and names which should be investigated include KW Electronics, Icom, Trio, Yaesu, Swan and Sommerkamp.

Whether one buys a new or second-hand RX is often a question of finance. A good used RX may sometimes be purchased for less than £100 whereas a new model could cost several hundred pounds, and four-figure sums are not unknown. Adverts for used equipment are to be found in the short wave radio press. It is best to buy a new RX from a specialist amateur radio dealer who will understand the complexities of what he is selling and wish to protect his reputation. Don't forget that the cost of the RX need be the only major expenditure by the listener: one needs power to run it, of course, but one doesn't have to keep buying films, video cassettes or petrol as in the case of some other hobbies!

Examples of RXs available in 1986 are given below, though it is emphasized that the list is not exhaustive. New models appear periodically.

TRIO R-2000

Coverage 150 kHz to 30 MHz in 30 bands (with optional VC10 converter for 118 to 174 MHz). Modes: SSB (USB/LSB), CW, AM, FM. Ten memories storing frequency, band and mode data for pushbutton recall of stations. Scanning facility. Digital frequency display to 100 hertz. 24-hour clock with timer. Three built-in IF filters with narrow/wide selector switch. Noise suppression circuitry. 4 in (10.2 cm) internal speaker. AGC. S-meter calibrated in RST and SINPO codes. High-impedance and low-impedance antenna terminals. Operates from 100/120/220/240v AC or 13.8v DC power supply. Headphone and recording output jack.
Price (mid-1987): £554 + VAT (£148 + VAT for VC10 converter). Details supplied by Lowe Electronics Ltd, Chesterfield Road,

Trio R-2000 receiver (Lowe Electronics Ltd).

Matlock, Derbyshire, DE4 5LE, from whom further information may be obtained. A new trio model, the R-5000, was introduced in late 1986.

YAESU FRG-8800

Coverage 150 kHz to 30 MHz (with optional FRV-8800 converter for 118 to 174 MHz). Modes: AM, SSB (LSB/USB), CW, FM. Digital

Yaesu FRG-8800 receiver (South Midlands Communications Ltd).

QRG display to 100 hertz. S-meter for RST and SINPO reports. Twelve internal memories (including mode data) and multi-function scanner. AGC and noise blanking filters. 24-hour clock with automatic timer for display, switching on RX and recording purposes. Squelch, tone and attenuator controls. Internal speaker with 1.4w audio output. Power: 100/120/220/240v AC 50/60 Hz. Optional 12v DC operation. Headphone and recording jack. May be used with personal computers for additional facilities and compatible with FRA-7700 Active Antenna and FRT-7700 Antenna Tuner.

Price (mid-1987): £538 + VAT (£87 + VAT for FRV-8800 converter).

Details supplied by South Midlands Communications Ltd, S.M. House, School Close, Chandlers Ford Industrial Estate, Eastleigh, Hants, SO5 3BY, from whom further information may be obtained.

ICOM IC-R71A

Coverage 100 kHz to 30 MHz. Modes: SSB, AM, CW, RTTY (FM optional). Digital QRG display to 100 hertz. Thirty-two programmable memory channels for recall of stations. Scanning facility. AGC and noise blanker provide clear reception through QRM. Preamplifier. S-meter. Headphone and recording jack. Power: 117v or 235v +/- 10% 50/60 Hz. Audio output more than 2 watts.

Icom R71E receiver (Thanet Electronics Ltd).

The mid-1987 price of the basic RX was £717.40 + VAT.
There are various optional extras available with this RX at additional cost. These include FM, synthesized voice frequency readout, infrared remote controller, adaptor for 12v DC operation, various filters, computer interface/terminal unit, external speaker, *etc.*
The popular IC-R70 model has been discontinued but may still be available.
Details supplied by ICOM (UK) Ltd, Unit 9, Sea Street, Herne Bay, Kent, CT6 8LD, from whom further information may be obtained.

JAPAN RADIO COMPANY NRD-525

Coverage 90 kHz to 34 MHz (with optional CMK 165 converter for 34 to 60 MHz, 114 to 174 MHz and 423 to 456 MHz). Modes: SSB (USB/LSB), CW, AM, FM, RTTY. Three built-in filters to assist selectivity of reception. Memory capacity of 200 channels (QRG, mode, bandwidth, AGC setting, attenuator on/off). Scanning facility. 24-hour clock and timer (which will also switch on a remote tape recorder). High-impedance and low-impedance antenna terminals. Digital frequency display to 10 hertz. S-meter. Headphone jack. Power: 100/120/220/240v AC or 13.8v DC.

JRC NRD-525 receiver (Lowe Electronics Ltd).

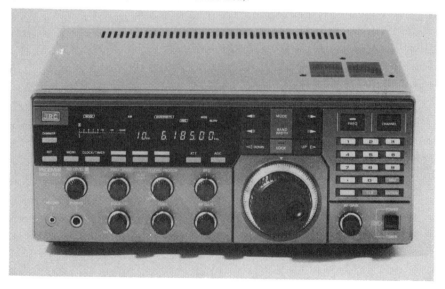

Price (mid-1987): £1039 + VAT (£340 + VAT for CMK 165 converter).
Details supplied by Lowe Electronics Ltd (address above).

The writer gratefully acknowledges the assistance provided by Messrs Lowe Electronics Ltd, South Midlands Communications Ltd and Thanet Electronics Ltd in supplying the above information.

Antennas

Having obtained our RX the next step is to introduce it to a satisfactory antenna. In this respect listeners are more fortunate than the transmitting stations, for the latter will spend a great deal of time and money in erecting the very best antennas that they can utilize so that their transmissions will be heard by the widest audience. This applies not only to broadcasting stations but to amateurs as well. Many stations have more than one antenna so that they can direct their transmissions to areas of the world on a selective basis. Antenna construction is very much a fine art and it is hardly surprising that some amateur enthusiasts spend more of their time on designing and testing antennas than in actually transmitting.

By contrast, listeners can get away with virtually anything! Even so, there is a good case for looking at the situation seriously and erecting as good an antenna as possible, but it is very easy to get started with an aerial of the utmost simplicity.

Most receivers are designed in such a way that an external antenna may be attached to the appropriate control at the back of the cabinet. Whilst there may be no sound coming from the RX without an aerial being attached, it is well known that the human body can act as an aerial of sorts, and a person who rests a finger on the antenna terminal will often find that many signals can be received at acceptable volume. This method of operating is not recommended, however, and not only because it is very difficult trying to operate a receiver with one hand firmly pressed to the back of the cabinet! It makes an amusing demonstration but will never take the place of more orthodox practices.

Before dealing with receivers which do need an external antenna for proper operation we could look at RXs which contain their own in-built aerial system. These sets are almost always of the portable variety. Their antennas vary in efficiency and the systems employed in the cheaper sets are often inadequate. Up-market models by major manufacturers are generally very much better. Whatever the position, performance will normally be improved — and sometimes improved immensely — by the addition of an external antenna and this possibility should always be considered. Portable sets frequently rely on a telescopic aerial which can be folded up when not in use. If this aerial is extended to its full length and then attached to another, longer aerial (preferably one which is mainly out of doors) there will sometimes be a noticeable improvement in the signal strengths of the stations being heard; this could be confirmed with the S-meter on the RX if there is one. The two separate aerials should be attached to each other so that the external one does not move — this could cause interference to the reception.

Where receivers have antenna terminals for the attachment of external wires it is as well to check with the manual in case any particular type of aerial is recommended. If it is not, one has to bear in mind the general 'rules' regarding aerials for short wave reception. Fortunately these are fairly simple.

There are optimum lengths for antenna wires in relation to the frequencies which are to be heard. This is worth considering by amateur bands listeners since long wire antennas designed for 20 metres will also work well on 40 metres and reasonably well on 80 metres, because 40 m is 2 × 20 m, *etc.* This arrangement does not help us a great deal on the broadcast bands with the main wavelengths being 19, 25, 31 metres, *etc.* For the BC bands what is needed is an antenna of sufficient length to provide satisfactory reception on all of the main bands, and the length often chosen is 50 ft (15.24 m) though this is by no means critical and any length from, say, 30 ft (9.14 m) to 100 ft (30.48 m) would work well.

Where it is desired to listen to a particular band, the policy is to have an antenna which is either a half or a whole wavelength of the wanted band. Consequently, for 20 metres a wire either 10 m (33 ft) or 20 m (66 ft) long would be best. Ideally, this should be erected out of doors as high as possible and clear of any obstructions. Whilst the direction of the wire will have some influence on the area which will be best received it will not be a critical factor and all areas are likely to be received acceptably. The antenna can be attached to the RX terminal directly or via an antenna tuning unit (ATU) which will often be bought as an add-on unit to the RX.

Modern receivers sometimes have built-in tuning units which provide a means of tuning the aerial to the frequency which is being heard. These are often in the form of RF tune and IF tune controls

Basic designs of receiving antennas.

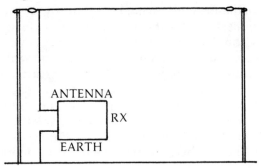

Inverted L antenna

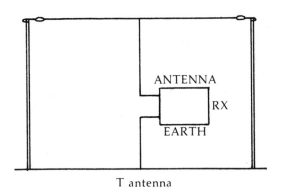

T antenna

Sloping wire antenna

and will indicate approximately the settings for each band. One needs firstly to tune the RF (radio frequency) for maximum signal strength and then peak the signals using the IF (intermediate frequency) control. Adjustments will have to be made as one tunes from one end of the band to the other. Used correctly, aerial tuning units are an invaluable aid to reception.

Although we cannot always choose the location of our homes with the requirements of radio reception in mind, locations at a high altitude over the surrounding area are always to be preferred and those in valleys can have serious drawbacks. In all circumstances the higher the antenna above ground the better the reception is likely to be, though one must remember that a very high aerial could fall foul of the local planning regulations and may lead to a demand for it to be taken down. Another factor which one needs to consider is that nearby power lines will cause electrical interference which could make listening extremely difficult, especially in damp weather.

Types of antennas which could be usefully employed by short wave listeners are shown in the illustration. These are basic designs and in due course the listener may well be tempted to experiment with something more elaborate. Where antenna wires are attached to masts this needs to be done using ceramic insulators so that the wire does not come into direct contact with the masts. Bare wire or covered wire may be used; the former obviously must not make any contact with metal objects such as window frames.

It is always preferable to have an outdoor antenna wherever this is possible but that obviously creates problems for people whose

Vertical rod antenna

ANTENNA

EARTH

houses do not have gardens or whose gardens are too small to accommodate a long wire, which really needs to be at least 30 ft (9 m) long for adequate reception over a wide range of frequencies. In these circumstances one can attach a vertical rod to the side of the house as shown in the illustration; the length of the rod should be around 5 m (16 ft 6 in).

Although almost all receivers are designed to operate with an earthing system, it is quite common for listeners not to take advantage of this arrangement. An adequate earth will in some cases reduce interference from electrical sources and it is an important safety device during periods of atmospheric disturbance such as thunder and lightning. If an earthing system is to be used, though, it must be efficient. The usual method is to drive a long stake into the ground and to attach the earth wire to that, with the other end going to the earth terminal on the receiver. The length of wire involved needs to be short (less than 30 ft (9 m) as an absolute maximum) and if that is not possible it might be best to dispense with the earthing system. Attaching earth wires to domestic water pipes, which was widely advocated in years gone by, is not regarded as a reliable method nowadays and could even be unsafe. If that is one's only possibility it is best to forget about the earth altogether.

For those listeners with no possibility of erecting an outdoor antenna, which will often include people living in multi-storey blocks of flats, all is not completely lost (though flat-dwellers may have to contend with more QRM than others). Indoor antennas can be made to work well and good reception is quite possible. I used a 33 ft (10 m) indoor antenna for many years and it brought me reception of more than 200 countries.

Apart from the telescopic aerials used by portable sets and referred to earlier, an indoor antenna needs to be of a sufficient length to provide satisfactory service. For reception of the 21 and 28 MHz bands a length of less than 10 m (33 ft) might be suitable but for most people 33 ft will be the minimum. To spread such a length of wire around the living room is sure to attract adverse comment and it will not look particularly elegant in the radio shack (room set aside for radio equipment) either. It could rest on the floor beneath the table but for best results it needs to be as high as possible and not screwed up into a ball! Wherever possible, the answer is to place the main part of the aerial in the loft, with down-wire coming through the loft door to the RX which should be located as near to the loft door as possible to prevent innocent visitors from strangling themselves! Such an arrangement can be made to work very well and it need not be untidy if the whole thing is properly thought out. A typical attic will generally accommodate 33 ft of wire in a straight line, but it is far better to bend the direction of the wire rather than to abandon the idea if it will not.

As with outdoor antennas, indoor wires offer considerable scope for experimentation and there is a great sense of achievement in hearing DX stations in less-than-ideal circumstances. At the other end of the scale, listeners who are really keen and have the ability to do so (both in terms of money and lack of opposition from neighbours or local council) may use beam antennas which can be rotatable to concentrate on particular parts of the world whenever required. Antennas of this type are understandably popular with transmitting amateurs but few SWLs use them. They are ideal for contests, when one has to listen for certain countries a considerable distance away, but they do have the disadvantage for the average listener that they are so directional that interesting stations from other areas away from the beam setting will not be heard and these stations could be even more desirable than the ones actually being received. Listeners who opt for beams, which are only made commercially for the amateur bands, would do well to have an alternative antenna as well. They can then pick out the area of the world which shows the most promise from the non-directional antenna before switching to the beam for much better reception from that area.

Amateur Radio Operating Procedure and Identification of Stations

Radio amateurs and short wave listeners are frequently called upon to demonstrate their hobby to friends. Some time ago a visitor to my home asked to see the radio rig in operation. It was early evening and the reception conditions were such that several countries liberally scattered throughout the world were heard in the space of a few minutes. Asked for his opinion of the demonstration, the novice listener looked puzzled. He admitted that it all sounded very interesting but then had to concede that he really hadn't understood very much of what he had heard.

There was no trickery involved. The visitor hadn't been exposed to CW transmissions which he could not have been expected to understand. All of the amateur stations heard had been using telephony (SSB) and most of them had had reasonably strong signals. There were two reasons for his confusion: firstly, his hearing was not attuned to reception of SSB and, secondly, he could not interpret several of the expressions which were being used.

Most regular listeners have grown up with SSB and set their receivers for maximum intelligibility. They also develop the knack of being able to concentrate on hearing one station although there may be other stations nearby which are also audible. It takes time to master this ability, as is often shown by newcomers who report hearing stations which they have incorrectly identified. In a rush of initial enthusiasm it is so easy to misread callsigns or to hear one side of a contact (QSO) and believe one is hearing the other. Very often both sides of a conversation can be heard but there are many times when this does not happen.

Because most newcomers to listening do not know the morse code it is usual for SWLs to become acquainted initially with SSB transmissions. A contact in its simplest form would sound something like the following example. In this instance, a British amateur (whose callsign has been 'manufactured' for the purpose of this item) puts out a general call and is answered by another British amateur on the 80 metres amateur band. (G7 call signs are expected to be introduced in 1987 or 1988.)

First station: CQ CQ CQ. CQ 80 CQ 80 CQ 80 metres. This is G7AAA G7AAA George-Seven-Alpha-Alpha-Alpha George-Seven-Alpha-Alpha-Alpha. This is George-Seven-Alpha-Alpha-Alpha calling CQ 80 metres and standing by for a call.

Second station: G7AAA G7AAA G7AAA. This is G7XYZ G7XYZ George-Seven-Xray-Yankee-Zulu George-Seven-Xray-Yankee-Zulu calling you and standing by.

First station: G7XYZ. George-Seven-Xray-Yankee-Zulu. This is George-Seven-Alpha-Alpha-Alpha replying. Thank you for your call, old man. You are 5 and 9 here. Q5 S9 — a very good signal. My name is Alan and I'm located in Birmingham. I'm using a Fox-Tango-901 and a dipole antenna. We have sunny weather here in Birmingham and the temperature is around 60°. How do you copy me? G7XYZ G7AAA.

Second station: G7AAA from G7XYZ. Fine business on your transmission, Alan. You are also Q5 S9 here. My QTH is London and my name is Bill. I'm using a Yaesu Fox-Tango-301-Delta running 200 watts to a long wire antenna. It's raining here in in London. Many thanks for the QSO. Please QSL via the QSL Bureau. Seventy-three. G7AAA G7XYZ.

First station: Seventy-three, old man. See you down the log. G7XYZ G7AAA.

Yes, it is hardly surprising that a newcomer may find this type of conversation somewhat mystifying. Let us now analyze the various components of it.

When an amateur transmits a 'CQ call' he is inviting any other amateur in the world to reply to him. The respondent could be in the same street or in Timbuctoo! However, if he wants to speak only with rare or long-distance stations he needs to call 'CQ DX', which indicates that he will not normally reply to stations in nearby countries. One person's opinion of what constitutes DX may not be shared by another and the definition will change from band to band. As a rule of thumb, stations calling CQ DX will not normally expect to be answered by stations within their own continent. Of course, there is nothing to stop the station being more precise. If he wants to talk to (or 'work', to use the standard jargon) only stations in Australia he will call 'CQ VK', VK being the prefix for Australia.

Each amateur station is allocated a callsign by the licensing authorities of his country and has to use this on the air to identify himself. Stations in England are allocated the prefix 'G', followed by a number and either a two- or three-letter suffix. (Callsigns will be explained in more detail later.) In this example both stations are located in England and therefore have 'G' prefixes. To prevent any mishearing of the callsigns, and indeed other information, the callsigns are always given periodically using the phonetic alphabet. When it is clear that both stations have copied each other's callsign exactly there is obviously no need for continued use of phonetics.

Regular listeners may be forgiven for thinking that there are countless phonetic alphabets. Some people seem to devise their own! This is not really a problem if they serve the intended purpose and many of them do. After all, the whole idea of phonetics is that they enable the other party to understand the information he is given. The recommended phonetic alphabet is given below:

A Alpha	H Hotel	O Oscar	U Uniform
B Bravo	I India	P Papa	V Victor
C Charlie	J Juliet	Q Quebec	W Whiskey
D Delta	K Kilo	R Romeo	X X-ray
E Echo	L Lima	S Sierra	Y Yankee
F Foxtrot	M Mike	T Tango	Z Zulu
G Golf	N November		

Shakespeare fans will appreciate the Romeo and Juliet bit!!

Another popular method is to use phonetics based exclusively on countries or cities. Thus the first five letters are sometimes rendered as America, Baltimore, Canada, Denmark and England. The only problem with this one is finding somewhere which begins with the letter 'X'!

Stations need to know how well their signals are being received and this is where the reception reports come in. These include three components, namely Readability, Strength and Tone, and are given using the RST Code. The tone of a signal is not relevant to telephony transmissions and only the first two reports are given for AM and

SSB stations and are sometimes referred to as 'QSA and R' or 'Q and S' rather than 'R and S'. The full RST code is given below:

Readability

R1 Unreadable
R2 Barely readable, occasional words distinguishable
R3 Readable with considerable difficulty
R4 Readable with practically no difficulty
R5 Perfectly readable

Signal strength

S1 Faint, barely perceptible
S2 Very weak signals
S3 Weak signals
S4 Fair signals
S5 Fairly good signals
S6 Good signals
S7 Moderately strong signals
S8 Strong signals
S9 Extremely strong signals

Tone

T1 Extremely rough hissing note
T2 Very rough a.c. note, no trace of musicality
T3 Rough, low-pitched a.c. note, slightly musical
T4 Rather rough a.c. note, moderately musical
T5 Musically modulated note
T6 Modulated note, slight trace of whistle
T7 Near d.c. note, smooth ripple
T8 Good d.c. note, just a trace of ripple
T9 Purest d.c. note

It will be seen, therefore, that Q5 R9 (or R5 S9, or Q5 S9!) indicates a perfectly readable and extremely strong signal. Where signals are exceptionally strong they may be described as strength 9+ or strength 9 + 20, 40 or even 60 decibels. Unlike the Readability and Strength characteristics, which depend on factors often beyond the control of the amateur, the Tone of his CW signal should be T9 in all instances and if that is not the case he will wish to make some modifications to his equipment. In practice, many amateurs exaggerate the reports given to other stations, sometimes wildly;

one often hears requests for information to be repeated by stations who are allegedly 'perfectly readable'.

If a station's signals are not being copied with clarity it is often necessary for him to spell out such things as his name and location. This also applies where the other station may not be familiar with these details. Whilst an overseas station will surely know the location of London and Birmingham, he may not be familiar with smaller places and will need to have the names of these places told to him using the phonetic alphabet.

All stations like to know what equipment is being used by those to whom they talk; they may even be using the same equipment themselves and will want to exchange notes. Where contact is exceptionally difficult due to QRM or of a quick-fire nature, as in a contest, details of equipment will not normally be given, however. Details of the weather (WX) may or may not be given depending on the operator. If temperature is quoted it may be either in Fahrenheit or Celsius (centigrade), depending on what will be understood by the other station.

At the end of each QSO it is courteous for each station to confirm the contact by sending what is known as a 'QSL card'. This aspect of the hobby, which also involves listeners, is discussed in the chapter on Verifications.

It should be particularly noted that where the callsigns of both stations are given together, the callsign of the transmitting station is given *last*. 'G7AAA G7XYZ' means that G7XYZ is passing the transmission over to G7AAA. This rule is occasionally broken by inexperienced operators and cannot be regarded as wholly reliable. As an alternative, 'G7AAA G7XYZ' could actually be given as 'This is G7XYZ turning the transmission over to G7AAA', which is also acceptable. There are obvious pitfalls here for SWLs listening to stations in foreign languages.

The term '73' used at the end of a QSO means 'best wishes'. 'FB' or 'fine business' means that everything has been copied well. Another abbreviation which is regularly used is 'HI', which indicates that a comment is intended to be amusing. 'Old man' (OM) is not a comment on the age of the operator but purely a colloquialism. Likewise, '88' (defined as 'love and kisses' and addressed to a member of the opposite sex) should not be interpreted too literally! As we shall see, many of these terms originated in the days when almost all contacts were made by morse code and brevity was very much a virtue.

One of the main sources of abbreviations used in amateur radio (and occasionally in broadcast radio) is the International Q-Code. This was devised for CW transmissions and each abbreviation can be transmitted either as a question or as an answer. For instance, 'QRV?' asks 'Are you ready?' and 'QRV' (without the question mark) answers 'I am ready'.

Some of the Q-code items are also used with telephony. A list of these Q-Code abbreviations with their CW and telephony uses is given in Appendix 6, and a list of the more general abbreviations used in short wave radio will be found in Appendix 7.

QSOs using the morse code contain the same kind of information as telephony contacts. Some people will be familiar with morse from activities unconnected with radio but others need to start from scratch. Stations using low power frequently perform better on CW than SSB and there is much to be gained from learning to copy the code. For those intending to become radio amateurs with permission to operate on all bands it is absolutely essential. The morse code is reproduced in Appendix 5.

Some local amateur radio clubs run classes for their members wishing to learn morse and the possibility of attending evening classes organized by local authorities should also be investigated. Many people find it easier to learn in a group atmosphere than in trying to study by themselves. For those who cannot avail themselves of organized classes it is possible to learn by purchasing records or cassettes.

Let us now look at a typical CW QSO. For comparison purposes we will assume that the QSO between G7AAA and G7XYZ, which we have just examined, is taking place on CW. It will be seen that the same information can be conveyed quite economically using standard abbreviations and operating procedure. The only significant difference is that the report to a CW station needs to include not only Readability and Signal Strength (as for a telephony station) but also the Tone of the signal. The QSO will sound like this:

First station:	CQ CQ CQ CQ 80 DE G7AAA G7AAA K
Second station:	G7AAA G7AAA DE G7XYZ G7XYZ AR
First station:	G7XYZ DE G7AAA MNI TNX FER CALL OM = UR RST 599 NAME ALAN ES QTH BIRMING-HAM = TRX FT901 ES ANT IS DIPOLE = WX SUNNY TEMP 60 F = HW CPY? AR G7XYZ DE G7AAA K

Second station: G7AAA DE G7XYZ R FB ALAN = UR RST 599 =
                   QTH LONDON ES NAME BILL = RIG YAESU
                   FT301D 200W ANT IS LONG WIRE = WX
                   RAIN = MNI TNX FER QSO = PSE QSL VIA
                   BURO = 73 AR G7AAA DE G7XYZ VA
First station: G7XYZ DE G7AAA R 73 BILL ES CUAGN = VA
                   G7XYZ DE G7AAA

Much of this will be self-explanatory when compared with the telephony contact, but comment must be made about those features which are peculiar to CW.

At the end of each transmission the station concerned has to indicate his intentions. 'K' means that he is passing the transmission to another station for a reply. 'AR' indicates the end of a transmission but not the end of the contact. At the final stage both stations send 'VA' which means that the QSO has terminated. Both 'AR' and 'VA' are sent as single characters in these circumstances (AR = di-dah-di-dah-dit and VA = di-di-di-dah-di-dah) and it is amusing to find that some stations close their telephony QSOs by imitating the CW by voice! 'R' (rendered as 'Roger' on telephony) means 'message understood'.

The QSOs described are of course very basic and readers may well feel that there cannot be a great deal of satisfaction in someone in Birmingham finding out that it is raining in London. If that is all amateur radio is about, surely there is no point in having amateurs in Manchester, for doesn't it rain there all the time?

This brings us on to one of the two questions most often asked about amateur radio: what do amateurs (or, more likely, 'hams', but let's not go into that again!) talk about? It would in fact be easier to indicate what they do not discuss since only the most sensitive topics are barred. We must remember that amateur radio is an international hobby and views which may be held in Britain may be objectionable to people in other countries – and of course vice versa. For this reason amateurs are prohibited from talking about politics or religion, both of which lead to wars with some regularity but which are liable to upset people even if they do not. Russian stations are extremely active in amateur radio but they do not make any reference to their country's political system and neither do the stations with whom they are in contact. Likewise, two stations located in a country in which there are several religious factions would not make any comment about the situation and certainly not give their views on it.

Contravention of these rules would render the offender liable to lose his transmitting licence. That is not to say that religion and politics cannot be mentioned in any shape or form; one quite often hears stations say that they have just returned from church or that they have voted in an election.

Quite obviously conversations are supposed to be conducted in a polite manner and a serious view would be taken of anyone using offensive language. But with that proviso, and the embargo on politics and religion, amateurs are free to talk about any topic which interests them. As a scientific hobby it is not surprising that many conversations revolve around the theory of radio itself, with amateurs comparing receivers, antennas and various accessories which they use or are available on the market. Where they have different types of equipment (especially antennas) they quite frequently test them on the air and get comparative reports. Certainly they discuss the weather (or at least make mention of it). Some of the most interesting QSOs take place between amateurs who know each other's countries and can compare their views.

Amateurs are not allowed to transmit messages for general reception in the way that broadcasting stations do, neither may they transmit music. They must confine their activities to conversations with other amateur stations. The only exceptions to this are where national radio societies are given permission to broadcast news bulletins about short wave radio activities or practice sessions for their members learning the morse code.

Some countries (most notably the United States) allow third-party traffic on the amateur bands. In these instances, known as 'phone patches', two amateurs assist people in their respective countries to talk to non-amateur friends and relatives by relaying telephone conversations via amateur radio. This facility, which is not available in Europe, is seemingly less used now than a few years ago and those amateurs who object to amateur radio being used for this purpose would not be sorry to see the back of it altogether.

Amateur radio is sometimes used as a means of members of the same family keeping in touch with each other. One can regularly hear QSOs between the UK and overseas countries with strong links with Britain where the amateur in England may well be the father of the amateur in, say, Zambia. Indeed, some people endeavour to obtain transmitting licenses in the UK before leaving for abroad as this generally makes it easier for them to become licensed as amateurs when they get to their new location. Most countries, including

Britain, will not allow an amateur station to be operated by anyone without a transmitting licence, even under the closest supervision, so the amateur in Zambia would not be able to talk to the whole of the family unless everyone was licensed, but he could of course speak to them in general terms with the father (in this example) passing along the replies on their behalf.

Before we move on to types of QSO other than the conventional straightforward conversation which lasts just as long as there are topics to discuss, we must consider how to identify the stations we are hearing. We have already seen that stations in England have callsigns beginning with the letter 'G', but what about other countries?

Each amateur station is issued with a callsign by the relevant authorities of the country where he is located and this callsign not only indicates the country but the identity of the individual station. There have been instances where callsigns have been issued more than once (though not at the same time) but this is comparatively rare. Generally speaking, once an amateur has been issued with a call it is his exclusively unless and until it is changed by the authorities. These changes do not happen willy-nilly and many amateurs keep the same calls for all time.

Explaining the composition of callsigns makes the whole thing sound terribly complicated whereas it is in reality very simple to identify almost all of the stations which one hears on the bands. Basically, a callsign (often known just as a 'call'), consists of three parts:

(a) a prefix (PX) which identifies the country. This consists of a single letter, two letters, a letter and a numeral or a numeral and a letter. Examples are G (for England), LA (Norway), A9 (Bahrain) and 7P (Lesotho).

(b) a numeral. This may identify a particular region of a country, be a guide to when the callsign was issued, or have no particular significance. In some instances the numeral has to be considered together with the prefix and is often referred to as part of the prefix.

(c) a suffix which identifies the particular station. This may be of a single letter, two letters or three letters.

There are some exceptions to these general rules which will be discussed later, but they do not normally hamper identification.

The prefixes are issued in blocks by the International Tele-communications Union (a United Nations agency) and apply to all radio stations, not only to amateurs. Armed with the country block allocations, which are given in Appendix 1, it is possible to identify the country of a station or at least to establish the 'parent' country where a block is given to a country and its overseas possessions. For example, JYA to JYZ is allocated to Jordan, and any station with a JY prefix can only be in that country. Likewise, APA to ASZ is given to Pakistan, so stations with AP, AQ, AR and AS prefixes would be in Pakistan; at the present time only AP is used since there are few amateurs in Pakistan and there is no need for the full range of prefixes to be employed. However, it is quite common for stations to use special calls from time to time, especially in contests or to celebrate some event of national importance, and when an unusual prefix is being used one needs to refer to the ITU list since few people are able to memorize the entire contents of it. Should a station appear using the call AS1AA and claiming *not* to be in Pakistan, it is fairly certain that he is an imposter (or 'pirate' in radio jargon) and not worthy of attention. Fortunately such 'pirates' are not very prevalent; 1 April is a good day to hear them and they often claim to be in Albania, from where there has been no legal amateur activity for very many years!

Within the block allocations a few prefixes are used by more than one country (as recognized for radio purposes), but this problem is declining. The JAA-JSZ block allocation is held by Japan; amateur radio is very popular in that country and in addition to the JA prefix Japanese amateurs also use JE, JF, JG, JH, JI, JJ, JK, JL, JM, JN and JR and will no doubt use up other prefixes before long. JD has a special significance in that it is used by stations on the Japanese islands of Minami Torishima (formerly Marcus Island) and Ogasawara Islands (ex-Bonin & Volcano Islands). From the callsign it is not possible to determine the location of JD-stations but as there are very few of them serious DXers will often know the details.

The United Kingdom has three block allocations: GAA to GZZ, MAA to MZZ and 2AA to 2ZZ, with only the first being used by the amateur service. (Other blocks are allocated to British overseas possessions.) This nevertheless provides ample scope: G is used for England, GD for the Isle of Man, GI for Northern Ireland, GJ for Jersey, GM for Scotland, GU for Guernsey and GW for Wales. Some special callsigns for stations operating from exhibitions, special events, *etc.*, are allocated a GB prefix and are almost always temporary; these can present problems with location identification since they could be from anywhere within the British Isles.

The numerals used in all callsigns may or may not be of particular significance depending on the country concerned. Where countries have overseas territory, (*viz.* land which does not form part of the mainland) the numeral is likely to be of great importance since it will indicate in which 'country' (for radio purposes) the station is located. A good example of this can be found in the case of Spain, which has the block allocations EAA to EHZ and also AMA to AOZ, the latter not often used.

Spanish stations with full licences are given callsigns with the prefix EA. Other stations may use EB, EC, ED, EE, EF, EG and EH, the most common of which are EC and ED for stations with restricted licences which can operate only on certain bands. The ITU block allocation covers not only the Spanish mainland but also the Balearic Islands, the Canary Islands, and Ceuta & Melilla in North Africa. It is the numeral in the callsign which tells us the location of the stations. Stations with the figures 1, 2, 3, 4, 5 and 7 are in mainland Spain, whilst EA6 is used by the Balearic Islands, EA8 by the Canary Islands and EA9 by Ceuta & Melilla.

Although a Spaniard would no doubt argue that all of the above places are parts of Spain, for short wave radio purposes the Balearic Islands, the Canary Islands and Ceuta & Melilla (together) are regarded as separate 'countries' from Spain in the same way that England, Scotland, Wales, Northern Ireland, Jersey, Guernsey and the Isle of Man are all considered as separate countries and not merely linked together as one country under the heading 'British Isles', 'Great Britain and Northern Ireland', or whatever.

The subject of recognition of places as 'countries' in radio terms is a complicated one and arouses much argument. It will be discussed in detail in the later chapter, Measuring Achievements.

Many countries follow the example of Spain in using the callsign numeral to identify the part of the country in which the station is located. Very often, of course, the numeral has less significance for the country-chaser. In the case of Bolivia, for example, there are nine call districts but as they are all on the mainland of that land-locked country they all naturally count as Bolivia.

Those countries which do not adopt the 'district system' usually issue callsigns to new licensees in strict sequence alphabetically. In these cases they will probably use the same numeral for all callsigns and will not necessarily start at '1'. In the example of Lesotho, for instance, the prefix is 7P, the numeral invariably 8, and the suffix is a series starting at AA and continuing to ZZ. Consequently one can sometimes tell from the callsign how long a station has been licensed and probably pick out 'pirate' stations using callsigns which would not have been issued at a certain point in time. However, a station signing 7P3DD would not automatically be bogus because he was using the numeral '3' instead of the normal '8'; countries do occasionally change the numerals of their stations, generally for limited periods to celebrate some national event. The numeral would almost certainly be queried by stations in contact with 7P3DD unless the information had been widely circulated in advance. If 7P3DD were a genuine call it would originally have been issued as 7P8DD and used by the same operator.

It must not be assumed that the issue of callsigns will be in a totally logical manner, with 1AA to 1ZZ being followed by 2AA to 2ZZ, 3AA to 3ZZ and so on. The numerals may be issued out of sequence, as in the example of Britain. Here we now have the GØ series following the G4 series, which came after the G3 series. (The G7 series, used in our mock QSO earlier, has not yet been used.) There may well be good reasons for this since other series may have been allocated to other radio services such as aircraft and shipping.

Another use of the numeral, which also applies in our own country, is to identify different classes of licence. If we exclude callsigns with two-letter suffixes, which were issued many years ago, we can see that G2, G3, G4 and GØ are full licences allowing the operators full use of all amateur frequencies; G5 calls are reciprocal licences; and G1, G6 and G8 callsigns allow restricted use of the amateur bands by stations yet to obtain full licences.

The numerals which may be used are from one to nine and zero. The zero is always written 'Ø' and tends to be interpreted more as 'ten' than 'nought' since stations with a 'Ø' in their callsigns are usually listed after those with '1' to '9' from the same country. There are isolated instances where stations have two numerals in their callsign, such as HG19HB in Hungary, but this generally happens only in the case of special callsigns; 5B25, instead of the usual 5B4, was used to celebrate the twenty-fifth anniversary of the independence of Cyprus. But one must not confuse two numerals in the centre of a callsign with the situation where one of the numbers is in fact part of the prefix. A station in Botswana may have the callsign A22DX; in this case A2 is the prefix, 2 is the numeral and DX is the suffix.

Although most countries are now complying with the standard system, there are a few which do not, though it is likely that they will change before long. In these cases, the first *letter* after the prefix (which always contains a number) is equivalent to the numeral. An example is the Sultanate of Oman which uses the prefix A4 followed by the letter X and then the suffix, so that one might hear A4XZZ instead of the expected A41ZZ. It is worth bearing in mind that (with the sole exception of JY1, the personal callsign of HM King Hussein of Jordan) every amateur callsign contains one or two figures in its centre, be they part of the prefix or the numeral or both.

In Appendix 3 we list all amateur radio prefixes in normal use, together with the numerals which generally follow them (if appropriate). Where the numeral is an essential factor in identifying the radio country this is shown as though it were part of the prefix, and where the first letter of the suffix is also indicative of the country this is also shown as part of the prefix. Where there is only one callsign allocated to a radio country, as in the case of 4U1UN (United Nations, New York), this is shown in full.

The suffix of a callsign indicates the particular station and it may be of one, two or three letters. Countries which have many amateurs, with the important exception of the USA, usually use three-letter suffixes. It sometimes happens that countries use two-letter suffixes from AA to ZZ until these have been fully issued and then start on a three-letter series as the amateur radio population of a country grows, notwithstanding that some of the two-letter suffixes may have ceased to be used. Not all countries use their suffixes in sequence. Some issue callsigns based on the name of the operator, so that John William South may have the suffix JWS! Other stations who move from one country to another are sometimes allowed to retain the suffix which they have used previously if they so request.

Instances where the suffix is instrumental in identifying the country are declining as the number of prefixes increases, but some still remain. A good example of this occurs with VK9. VK is the prefix for Australia, and Australian overseas territories are given callsigns with the numeral '9' or 'Ø'. To identify where stations with a figure '9' are located one has to consider the first letter of the suffix: VK9L is Lord Howe Is, VK9M is Mellish Reef, VK9N is Norfolk Island, VK9X is Christmas Island, VK9Y is Cocos-Keeling Island and VK9Z is Willis Island. An added complication here is that novice stations without a full licence use the letter 'N' after the numeral '9', so that VK9NYY would be in Cocos-Keeling Island and not Norfolk Island, but stations in this category will rarely be heard. They will always have three-letter suffixes beginning with 'N', whereas a two-letter suffix would not belong to a novice station and would follow the normal rules,

An amateur radio QSL card from the author's collection.

VK9NY being in Norfolk Island.

A similar thing used to happen with stations in the Leeward and Windward Islands groups in the Caribbean, which all had the prefix VP and the numeral 2. As these countries have attained full independence they have generally changed their prefixes and the only VP2s now remaining are VP2E (Anguilla), VP2M (Montserrat) and VP2V (British Virgin Islands). St Kitts & Nevis has changed from VP2K to V4 and St Vincent from VP2S to J8, *etc.* A peculiarity with Argentina is that the first letter of the suffix indicates the region of the country.

Most countries these days have the reciprocal licensing arrangements referred to earlier whereby an amateur from one country may operate with permission in another country. In some instances the amateur will be given a callsign in the sequence used by the country he is visiting (*e.g.* a West German amateur in Britain would use a G5xxx call), but in other cases he will use his own call with an additional suffix indicating the country from which he is operating (*e.g.* G7AAA/C6A would be G7AAA operating from the Bahamas – lucky chap!). One therefore has to remember that a full callsign followed by the prefix of another country means that the station is actually located in the country represented by the final prefix.

If all this sounds ridiculously complicated — and let's admit that it

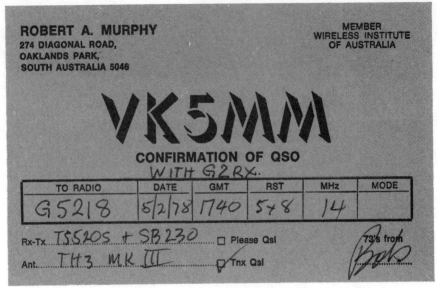

An amateur radio QSL card from Australia (Author's collection).

does! — it should not deter the listener, who will in practice find the system quite easy to understand after only a brief acquaintance. He will need to ensure that he has copied the callsign correctly and then look up the prefix in Appendix 3. If it is not listed, the likelihood is that the callsign has not been issued in the regular series and he will then have to turn up the ITU block allocation listed in Appendix 1. If that fails — and it rarely will — the only answer is to listen to the station until he actually says where he is located.

Mention has already been made of stations in the United States of America, and it has to be said that the system there is appallingly complex and has been branded as 'crazy' by a fair number of American amateurs themselves. Half of the world's radio amateurs are located in the USA and there are several classes of licence used there. The country is divided into ten call areas, from 1 to Ø, and each new licensee is allocated a callsign appropriate to the State in which he resides. For many years USA amateurs used prefixes with the letters 'K' or 'W' and when those series were fully used the WA, WB and WD series were brought into use. This system was very easy to follow and completely reliable; K1AA, W1AA, WA1AAA, WB1AAA and WD1AAA would all have been in the first call district comprising the States of Connecticut, Maine, Massachusetts, New Hampshire,

Rhode Island and Vermont. When a station moved from one call area to another on a permanent basis a new callsign was issued, but if the move was only temporary the same callsign was used but with an additional indication at the end (WA1AAA operating from the fifth call area would have been WA1AAA/Fixed Portable 5, which was understandable to other stations if questionable grammatically!).

The USA has several block allocations of callsigns and these are now being widely used. Very often stations have only one-letter suffixes, which delights the prefix hunters referred to later in the book, but doesn't make for simplicity. Any station now using the prefixes AA to AL, KA to KZ, NA to NZ and WA to WZ is located in the USA or a country over which the USA exercises authority. The prefixes AH, KH, NH and WH are used by stations in the Pacific Islands. AL, KL, NL and WL are used by Alaska. KP, NP and WP are used by islands in the Atlantic. Apart from this, all the prefixes are used by stations on the mainland of the USA. There is unfortunately some duplication: KC4, for instance, could be the States or an American base in Antarctica, and KG4 could be mainland USA or the American naval base at Guantanamo Bay, Cuba. It is hardly surprising that American stations consider the new system 'a goddam mess'... but that's not all! Once issued with a callsign, the station keeps it wherever he may be under US jurisdiction. This causes short-lived excitement when a station with a KH6 callsign, ostensibly in Hawaii, turns out to be in New York!

Whilst the call areas of the USA (along with those of other countries) are given in Appendix 4 for general information, they obviously need to be treated with more and more caution as time goes by. One guide to prefixes which may be used for more than one country is that stations with a single-letter suffix are most likely to be in the USA, but those with two-letter suffixes are probably in a US dependency. KV4P, for instance, would be in the States whereas KV4AA would be in the US Virgin Islands (which also use the KP2 prefix). This advice is not foolproof, however.

Listeners will sometimes hear stations who give their callsigns followed by the words 'Maritime Mobile'. This of course indicates that they are licensed amateurs operating from vessels. These persons use their own calls at all times and there is no way of knowing the location of the ship unless it is stated by the operator. A Japanese maritime mobile station could well be in British territorial waters! 'Maritime mobile' is also rendered as 'stroke MM' or 'Mickey mouse'. Amateurs operating from aircraft use their own callsigns followed by 'stroke AM' or 'Aeronautical Mobile' and the same situation applies; these are heard infrequently. Stations operating from vehicles on the roads will sign as 'Mobile' or 'stroke M', but they do use the callsigns issued by the countries where they are located so identification in these instances is no problem.

The callsign system had been covered in some depth because SWLs and amateurs want to know the locations of the stations which they are hearing. One could write far more on the subject but that would make things even more confusing. It is worth bearing in mind that stations almost always state their QTH during QSOs and it is advisable to wait for this information if there is any doubt. Radio magazines and bulletins often give details of unusual calls and this is another useful source of information.

Stations operating from the rarer parts of the world are obviously much in demand and attract a lot of attention. Where a listener finds very many stations all operating on the same QRG the chance is that they are all trying to obtain a contact with a DX station. Such stations generally try to be as helpful as possible in giving QSOs to other stations and often confine themselves to a quick exchange of signal report. It is not easy for them, of course. With hordes of stations calling in a typical 'pile-up' they have problems in reading the callsigns and will often adopt special procedures to get their contacts made.

'Working by call areas' or 'working by suffixes' is one such method. The DX station asks for calls from 'stations in the first call area' and then replies to callers with the figure '1' in the call, ignoring any other callers. He then continues with the other call areas from '2' to 'Ø'. Alternatively, he may ask for stations with the letter 'A' in the suffix, and so on. This system works satisfactorily if everyone co-operates, but it needs a very good DX operator to prevent things getting out of hand. If he were to reply to G7XYZ after asking for stations from the first call area that would be a sure recipe for pandemonium to break out!

With lots of stations all on the same QRG the chances of successful QSOs are somewhat limited and this is where 'split-frequency operation' comes into its own. The term simply means that the DX station operates on one frequency whilst inviting calls on another or maybe on a range of other frequencies. In these circumstances the DX station can be heard more clearly by all the callers because other stations are not calling whilst he is transmitting. (At least, that is the theory of it but regular listeners may be excused a wry smile!) Of course, the rare station will have to state at regular intervals where

An amateur radio QSL card from the Canary Islands (Author's collection).

he is listening otherwise more and more stations will start to call him on his transmitting QRG. Listeners who hear a 'pile-up' and cannot find the DX station on the same channel should tune around the frequency in case this type of split-frequency operation is taking place; the DX station, if audible at all, may well be found five to ten kilohertz lower than the calling stations (or even more) and they may have to wait for some time before the station actually gives his callsign if the QSOs are of a rapid nature.

Getting a QSO in these circumstances can be akin to a lottery. The calling stations running the highest power or with the most efficient antennas are likely to do better than other stations. In an effort to help everyone some DX stations make contacts on the basis of lists ('list operations'). There are some variations but the basic system is that a third party with a powerful station will collect the callsigns of stations who want to contact a particular DX station and then act as a go-between, calling in the stations one by one to speak to the DX station and generally endeavouring to keep things under control and deter gatecrashers. The list of stations is usually compiled some time in advance of the DX station being available – sometimes a couple of days in advance. At the pre-arranged schedule time the list controller

Station of W3ECR in the USA.

will call the DX station and, if he replies and is audible, will then call in
each station on the list to exchange signal reports. If propagation is
poor it may be impossible for the list operation to take place, in which
event the controller will have to decide whether to set up another
schedule.

Working to lists is a comparatively recent development and one
which has came in for plenty of criticism. It has often been suggested
that some of the stations on the lists would never be able to contact
the DX stations if left solely to their own devices. This is undoubtedly
true, though whether it is a valid point is open to debate. Certainly
one gets the impression that some stations guess the report they have
received and go on guessing it until they get it right! From a listening
angle we ought really to copy correctly two or three reports as a
minimum before being confident that we have properly heard the
station we want. Beware of amateurs who try, misguidedly, to help
by repeating reports for the benefit of others! This is totally
unethical.

In addition to pre-arranged list operations there are some of the
'instant' variety, especially on the LF bands. These sometimes become
quite comical affairs, especially where the list controller has more
enthusiasm than experience. Having worked a DX station he will tell
his counterpart that he will 'make a list' for him and then invite calls
from stations who want to contact the DX operator. This is

satisfactory where everyone knows what is happening but that isn't always the case. The DX station may not have agreed to work to a list — he may not even have been consulted — and he may go QRT immediately. (Some DX operators refuse categorically to work to lists and it is *their* prerogative.) Another danger is that the list becomes so long and takes so much time to compile that the propagation disappears or the DX man gets so tired of waiting that he gives up and goes to take the dog for a walk!

List operations have some similarities with 'nets', where a number of DX stations may be on the same QRG at the same time. Nets are regular operations taking place on the same QRG at the same time each day (but not always every day of the week) with the same net controller(s). The details are known to regular operators and other amateurs avoid the net frequencies when operations are in progress. At the outset all stations wishing to join the net are invited to identify themselves and listed in the order that they are heard by the net controller. At the commencement of the net proper, each station is called in turn to exchange reports with one or more of the other stations in the net. If there are many stations it is usual for only one contact to be allowed and it is unusual for more than two contacts per person in any circumstances.

A little earlier we mentioned one of the two questions most often asked by enquirers about amateur radio. It is not difficult to work out the other one: does everybody speak English and, if not, how can we understand them?

It is to be expected that two amateurs in the same country speaking to each other will use the language of that country; indeed, they may not know any other. However, for international QSOs the use of languages such as Danish or Serbo-Croat would clearly be inappropriate since few people would be able to understand them. This is not so, of course, with French, Spanish or German which are widely spoken throughout the world. An analysis of languages used for international contacts would undoubtedly show that the vast majority of them do take place in English, so that the SWL who knows no other language is very strongly placed compared with listeners who cannot speak English. There is clearly much to be gained by learning other languages, even if it is only the basics, to enable the callsigns of stations to be understood correctly. Nor is this difficult. Many experienced SWLs can identify stations in several languages even though they may not be able to understand anything other than the callsigns!

One of the benefits of CW is that the use of abbreviations which are accepted worldwide can enable an SWL to understand contacts which might be incomprehensible if they were in SSB. The numerals can be readily copied and so can the callsigns without any problems of accent or foreign vocabulary. The Russian station UA1WWQ would simply use the morse code to send that callsign in the conventional manner and perhaps with a signal report of '589', whereas on telephony these details would be rendered as 'Uljana Anna Odin Wassili Wassili Quka' and the report (without the Tone) as 'Pyartz Voseml'. And to make things even more tricky, the 'Quka' is pronounced as 'Schuka'!!

To listen to CW transmissions with maximum intelligibility one has to select the upper sideband (USB) mode on the receiver. Telephony stations operating on 14, 21 and 28 MHz also use the upper sideband whereas 'phone stations operating on 1.8, 3.5 and 7 MHz use the lower sideband, so the LSB mode should be selected when listening on these bands.

The High Frequency Amateur Bands Described

A thing which never ceases to amaze newcomers to the amateur bands — and some of the older hands too — is that each of the major HF bands has its own characteristics and differs, often appreciably, from all of the other bands. Most listeners who have been involved in the hobby for some time will have their favourite band on which they spend most time, but it is unusual for an SWL to specialize on one band to the exclusion of all others and anyone who does do so is missing a great deal of worthwhile listening.

Those listeners who enjoy local contacts, which may be between people they know personally, will probably favour 80 metres. Those who like to listen regularly, day in day out and year by year, are likely to prefer 20 metres for its consistency. Anyone who has heard 10 metres in full cry during the peak of the sunspot cycle will find anything else an anti-climax and may even give up the hobby during the lean years. And there's a band for masochists, too!

Advice to newcomers has not really changed over the years even though the hobby has developed. Since AM transmissions, which could be heard and understood on domestic receivers, have been all but eliminated from the amateur service during the past twenty-five years, newcomers need to acquire a communications RX if they are to be able to resolve SSB and CW stations. Such a receiver will almost certainly cover 10, 15, 20, 40 and 80 metres bands and may also include 160 metres. With this choice, where is the best place to start?

There is much to be said for commencing with the 80 metres telephony band and listening during daylight hours. The SWL won't hear any DX but he will find himself listening to very strong and clear British stations talking to each other in English. Because he will have no difficulty in hearing these stations he will be able to follow the conversations and get the feel of amateur radio; he will learn the codes, abbreviations and jargon and become familiar with the typical format of a QSO. One cannot claim that there is much excitement in this but it is good background information and some of the contacts will be quite interesting. Most people then progress to chasing DX and the recommended band for this is 20 metres since that range often carries long-distance stations when the others are closed. European stations will be very prevalent and South America will often be well represented. African and Asian stations will be heard from time to time, and during good conditions it will sometimes be possible to hear stations from Australia, New Zealand and the Pacific Islands. Naturally the signal strength of many of these stations will be lower than that of their British counterparts on 80 metres and there will be more QRM, making reception harder. But by this time the SWL will know what he is listening for and use his knowledge to good advantage.

The effect of the sunspot cycle on propagation has already been explained. At the peak of the cycle the conditions on 10 metres will border on the sensational, but at the other end of the scale it sometimes happens that not a single station is heard for several weeks. Fortunately, to compensate for this the lower frequencies come into their own at this time so there is a possibility of chasing DX at all times. In simple terms, when the higher frequencies of 21 and 28 MHz are poor the lower ones of 3.5 and 7 MHz are good and vice versa. The band least affected by the cycle is 14 MHz (20 metres) and this is why it is so suitable for those finding their feet in the hobby.

The eleven-year cycle does not operate in such a way that the bottom point is exactly half-way between peaks. It generally occurs around seven years after a peak; then there is a rise in sunspot activity leading to the next peak after another four years. At the time of writing the trough of the present cycle is expected around the end of 1986 or beginning of 1987, and in the following pages we will look at expected conditions on each band at both extremes of the cycle.

There are five major amateur bands used by almost all countries and these are the aforementioned 10, 15, 20, 40 and 80 metres (28, 21, 14, 7 and 3.5 MHz). 160 metres (1.8 MHz) is also well established but is not available universally. It is fair to say that the newest amateur bands of 30, 16 and 12 metres (10, 18 and 24 MHz) have not yet met with general acceptance and only on the first of the three is there any volume of traffic. We will deal with these so-called WARC bands after considering what the other frequency ranges have to offer.

1800–2000 kHz (160 metres)

This frequency range is known to its friends as Top Band because it is the highest wavelength used by radio amateurs. Indeed, it is closer to Radio Luxembourg on 208 metres medium wave than it is to the nearest amateur band of 80 metres. Because of this it carries some of the characteristics of the medium waves but is no less interesting for that.

Until the VHF bands became the norm for local contacts many of the cross-town QSOs used to take place on 160 metres. During daytime hours the distances covered were short and local stations were able to converse with each other without being bothered by QRM. Many friendships were made on this band. Later in the day contacts over greater distances were possible, though most of those were still confined to the British Isles. Transmitting power allowed to UK stations was only 10 watts and stations wishing to work into Europe usually used the CW mode which penetrated further than AM. The main obstacle to long-distance communication was the existence on the band of ship-to-shore stations and beacons which ran high power and obliterated parts of the band when they were transmitting.

Although they have decreased in numbers, and will continue to do so, the shipping stations are still a problem for British listeners on 160 metres. These stations officially share the band with radio amateurs and amateurs have to give them precedence. Some countries do not allow amateurs to use 160 metres and some, including the Scandinavian countries, allow CW but not telephony. There are many restrictions imposed by countries which do permit 160 metres operation and some provide less than 10 kilohertz for amateur use. Building up a big countries score on 160 metres is therefore very difficult and serious listeners regard it as an immense challenge to reach one hundred countries heard on the band. Very few SWLs have achieved this target, though it has become a little easier during the past few years as more countries have allowed 160 metres operation. SWLs who can read CW have a big advantage over those who listen only on SSB.

An event which undoubtedly led to a big upsurge in interest in Top Band was when Russian stations were given permission to use the band. The USSR is recognized as several 'countries' for short wave radio purposes and the influx of stations from European Russia, the Ukraine, Lithuania, Latvia, *etc.* provided listeners with several new countries almost at the drop of a hat. Admittedly, most of the Russian amateurs speak only in their own language but that is no great handicap for those prepared to listen carefully and there are of course some stations who also transmit in English. American stations have been more active on the band of late though they are by no means as common as on the other bands. They are generally to be found in the lower portion of the band (below 1860 kHz) whereas the Russians do not normally operate below 1860 kHz and are most easily heard between that QRG and 1940 kHz. There is not as a rule very much to hear at the top end of the band.

The sunspot cycle has less effect on 160 metres than on the other amateur bands, though it sometimes seems that conditions are marginally better at times of low sunspot activity. This may of course be due to more stations using the LF bands (by which we mean 160, 80 and 40 metres) when the HF bands of 20, 15 and 10 metres are quite poor. Long-distance reception generally starts around dusk with European stations being audible in the UK, and it is only when there is a full darkness path between Europe and North America that one would expect to hear USA and Canadian stations. South American stations appear infrequently and are most likely to be heard from around 0300 GMT to dawn. As soon as daylight arrives the DX disappears along with the European signals and a band which might have been full of long-distance stations at one moment can be completely deserted less than thirty minutes later. Before the band fades out there is sometimes a chance to catch New Zealand for just a few minutes. Other exceptional DX would include Japan around 2000 GMT from 1907.5 to 1912.5 kHz, Western Australia and Hong Kong between 2300 and 2400 GMT and, even more rarely, South Australia and Victoria around 2200 GMT.

For satisfactory DX reception on 160 metres it is necessary to have a reasonably good antenna. Long wires are particularly favoured, needing a minimum length of 132 ft (40 m). If conditions are exceptionally good 66 ft (20 m) might cope, but this length of wire is the shortest likely to be of use; it will bring in the Europeans but may well produce a total blank when it comes to transatlantic stations.

It is not unusual for those listeners tuning 160 metres to be confronted with a totally empty band. This often happens in the early evening when the local contacts have finished and the European stations have not yet become audible. If this does happen it is worth listening a few hours later and if the same situation applies one may as well go to bed! Best reception occurs in the autumn to spring period and it calls for a great deal of skill and perseverance to make progress during the months of April to September. Many SWLs do not bother with the band at all during this period.

The best times to listen to Top Band are, without any shadow of doubt, during major transmitting contests (which are discussed in a later chapter). At these times many stations are active and it is fairly easy to build up a reasonable score with some concentrated listening. Moreover, the main contests are held during the autumn to spring months when the LF conditions are at their best.

3500–4000 kHz (75 and 80 metres)

In Europe this amateur band runs from 3500 to 3800 kHz and is known as 80 metres, whereas in North and South America the frequency range used is from 3750 to 4000 kHz and therefore designated 75 metres. There are a great many variations for individual countries; generally the African and Asian stations use the same QRGs as the Europeans, with the rules in Australasia varying from country to country.

The 80 metres band (which we will call it for the sake of simplicity) has deservedly gained very many devotees during the past few years. Once regarded as a band mainly for local contacts and attracting few DX operators, it is now seen as one of the most exciting long-distance frequencies available to us. During the daytime it carries inter-UK and Western European QSOs with reliability and is very popular with stations wishing to discuss the technicalities of the hobby or to exchange notes about equipment. However, especially in winter, as darkness falls the skip distance of the signals increases and we are confronted with an entirely different situation with DX abounding. All this may come as a surprise to some of the local stations who occupy the band during the daytime and it is necessary to provide some words of qualification lest they all rush out and buy new receivers!

More and more countries are finding their way onto 80 metres but it still needs the right conditions for us to hear them. There is quite a variation in conditions from year to year but it is a poor year when one cannot log 100 countries on the band. My most successful year was in 1975 when I logged 155 countries and, at the time of writing, indications are that 1986 (eleven years later, be it noted!) will be slightly better. There was a sharp decline after 1975 and in 1978 only 103 countries were heard, with the score not starting to rise sharply until 1983.

As in the case of 160 metres, the best months for reception on 80 metres are from October to March, with December and January usually being the best of all. Indeed, keen 80 metres listeners often set themselves a challenge of hearing a century of countries on the band before the end of January and in a good year it is perfectly possible. January is a good month overall, with stations being heard from all round the world. Asian stations, including some from the Far East, may be heard in late afternoon with African stations starting to show from about 1930 GMT. Australia is possible from 1800 GMT. The first of the USA and Canadian stations will appear around 2100 GMT, with Caribbean area amateurs showing from 2230 GMT. The South Americans usually appear much later, from around 0300 GMT, and the propagation to the west will then continue until well after daylight. If conditions are particularly good, stations on the West Coast of the USA will be audible from 0700 GMT for an hour or so and at the same time stations in New Zealand may be heard. Of course, the times quoted in this paragraph are approximate and should not be considered wholly reliable; conditions can and do change from day to day and there may be days when nothing of interest is heard, but the times mentioned are a useful general guide.

In a poor year the conditions on 80 metres will decline rapidly after the first few weeks of the year but at other times the band will continue to provide fascinating listening until the end of March or even later. With the arrival of the lighter nights the DX possibilities decline sharply and local contacts dominate the band until midnight or later. Static interference can also be a problem, especially when there is obviously thunder in the air. However, it is still worth checking for DX and in the summer months the most likely reception path is to the south. Brazilian and other South American stations may be heard as early as 2200 GMT (2300 BST) and occasionally amateurs from southern Africa may be logged at the same time or even earlier. The transatlantic path tends to be unreliable during the summer but picks up in the autumn.

The reception pattern on 80 metres does not change very much from year to year. It is just that the propagation conditions are much better some years than others. Regular listeners to the band will often have more than 200 countries in their logs and will continue to get a few new ones each year as countries appear which have not previously been active on the band.

With the obvious exception of those countries which do not permit amateur radio, almost all other countries are allowed to use the 80 metres band but some of them are restricted in the frequencies which they may use. Until fairly recently USA telephony stations were not allowed to transmit below 3800 kHz and European amateurs could not (and still cannot) transmit above that QRG, with the result that all European/USA contacts were made using the split-frequency technique, but some classes of USA licence now allow W-station SSB operators to go as low as 3750 kHz. Canadian stations and operators in the Caribbean islands have always had the facility to operate above or below 3800, to their great benefit. Depending on the class of licence, USA stations are permitted to use CW from 3500 to 3775 kHz whereas European stations are restricted to 3500 to 3600 kHz, with the telephony band starting at 3600 and extending to 3800 kHz.

Russian stations are very keen on 80 metres but are normally restricted to the portion 3500 to 3650 kHz with the top 50 kilohertz allocated to telephony. This must be very frustrating for them since the bulk of the DX on the band is at least 100 kHz away and split-frequency operation is always difficult in these circumstances. One or two countries in the eastern Mediterranean use only 3695 to 3700 kHz and Indian stations operate as high as 3895 kHz. Australian stations used to have only around 3695 but do now operate at the top of the so-called 'European band' — around 3795 to 3800 kHz. The frequency ranges for some countries do change from time to time, which all adds to the confusion.

It is an unwritten rule that the 3790 to 3800 kHz segment of 80 metres is kept for DX working and a dim view is taken of European stations using that portion of the band for local contacts during the hours when DX QSOs are possible. Arguments are not infrequent. DX stations regularly work to 'lists' which allow the lower-powered stations to contact DX which might not otherwise be available to them. This is also of benefit to SWLs who might not otherwise be able to identify the DX stations and, in the main season, most listeners try to monitor that section of the band as often as possible. Most of the QSOs take place in English and it is comparatively easy to build a good score on 80 metres by knowing where to look. At busy times, the 3770 to 3790 kHz range also carries a fair amount of DX and so does the 'American band' from 3800 to 3840 kHz. American stations who operate above 3840 kHz generally confine themselves to contacts with other American stations, but one can get a few surprises from time to time and the whole of the 80 metres band should be regularly checked.

7000–7300 kHz (40 metres)

You either love this band or hate it! I fall firmly into the former camp and will have to be careful not to get too carried away. Hearing DX on 40 metres is a major challenge to any listener and there is more satisfaction in building up a good score here than on the other bands, with the possible exception of 160 metres.

The 'European band' covers from 7000 to 7100 kHz, with the lowest 40 kilohertz being allocated to CW only. This range is used not only by stations in Europe but by those in Asia, Australasia, Africa, South America and the Caribbean. For some non-European countries the upper limit is extended to 7110 kHz which allows split-frequency working away from the European QRM, and it is sometimes possible to hear telephony stations below 7040 kHz but rarely lower than 7030, where the CW stations dominate. USA stations use 7000 to 7150 kHz for CW and 7150 to 7300 kHz for telephony, with stations in Alaska and Hawaii also having the use of the top portion of the European band. South Americans and Caribbean area stations have the best allocation of frequencies since they can use both the European and American frequencies; the same also applies to Canada.

What makes 40 metres such a struggle for the serious DXer is that the band is shared with commercial broadcasting stations, some-times officially but in other instances simply because the BC stations choose to ignore the recommendations of the International Telecommunications Union. As many of these stations are in Europe and Asia and use very high powers, they do cause havoc to European listeners. The 7100 to 7300 kHz segment is a designated BC band so one cannot complain too strongly about the BC stations which operate there, but the same is not the case with 7000 to 7100 kHz and BC operators there are a genuine cause of grievance. Ironically, the worst culprit is Radio Tirana on 7030, 7065, 7075, 7080 and 7090 kHz, which churns out its programmes of political propaganda for many hours each day, the irony being that Albania is one of the very few countries which does not allow amateur radio by its nationals or visitors. The only obscene language I have ever heard on amateur radio has been directed towards this station!

40 metres has some similarities with the other LF bands, the main one being that it is a good local band in the daytime and turns into a DX band at night. Unlike 80 and 160 metres, however, it is not a reliable band for British contacts throughout the year and, especially in the winter months, it is often full of European stations from

Germany, Holland, Belgium and other countries from the west of the continent. More so than any other band, 40 metres appeals to listeners who have a knowledge of languages since the majority of the daytime contacts are not in English. After dark the European stations fade out and it is not uncommon to find the band completely devoid of amateurs in the early evening; it is not always much better later on and there are often times when monitoring the band is a complete waste of time. This is particularly so when the BC stations are taking up so much room.

Hearing 100 countries in a year on 40 metres is by no means assured and to achieve that objective will often call for a considerable amount of listening. My best year to date was 1982 when I heard 152 countries, compared with a minimum of 82 in 1976. At the time of writing, conditions on 40 metres are quite good; there were some superb openings in 1985, and 1986 also looked promising if slightly down on the previous year.

The best time of the year on this band tends to be during July and August when it is possible to hear all continents during some listening sessions. The band comes to life around 2200 GMT and the next few hours see excellent reception from South America and the Caribbean, together with Central America. Asian stations from the USSR and the Middle East also make a good showing and there is a fair sprinkling of stations from the African continent, mainly West Africa. From Oceania, Indonesian stations sometimes penetrate the QRM and Western Australia is a possibility. Surprisingly, USA stations tend to be hard to find in their section of the band (partly because of the BC QRM), though Canadians operating in the European band are heard regularly. When these openings occur one can so easily lose track of the time and turn up for work in the morning feeling much the worse for wear! During the big DX openings on 40 metres very few European stations will be heard and the listener has the satisfaction of logging the stations with little external assistance. Since the South Americans are frequently heard working other stations in the same continent, it is useful to have a basic knowledge of Spanish and Portuguese as this will aid identification. The Brazilian stations are the most numerous of the South Americans on the band and they of course speak in Portuguese, being the only stations on the continent to do so. It is easy after a while to distinguish between Portuguese and Spanish so one can concentrate on the Spanish-speaking stations which are likely to be from rarer countries.

Although the summer months are recommended for listening on 40 metres, DX is possible at all times. CW operators generally do better than the 'phone people and may be able to hear DX right round the clock — not greatly hindered by Radio Tirana! The winter months will sometimes provide DX from the Far East and Australasia in the middle of the afternoon, when SSB listeners would not dream of looking for it (and wouldn't hear it even if they did!). Autumn transmitting contests can also be most useful, not only for the CW fans but for SSB listeners too. At the end of the year it is sometimes possible to hear stations around sunset. It is always a good policy to monitor 40 metres (and indeed 80 metres also) at sunrise and sunset times at the listener's QTH.

14000–14350 kHz (20 metres)

The 20 metres band could fairly accurately be described as 'a band for all seasons'. Certainly it *is* affected by the sunspot cycle but less so than the other major HF bands of 15 and 10 metres, and there is no doubt that it is the most consistent amateur radio band of all. Scores of 200 countries in a year are regularly attainable and even less active listeners would expect to get more than 150 countries in a typical year.

One does not have the complications with frequency allocations that can confuse newcomers to the other bands. To avoid their stations swamping the whole of the band the USA authorities used to prohibit telephony operation below 14200 kHz, but they have had to relax this ruling as more and more stations have become licensed and some classes of licence now allow operation between 14150 and 14200 kHz in addition to the traditional frequencies. (This has not worked to the benefit of European listeners, who now find the frequencies used by non-USA stations are much more congested.) With that exception, all countries permit CW (telegraphy) operation between 14000 and 14100 kHz and SSB transmissions from 14100 to 14350 kHz.

A typical spring or autumn day during a year of average conditions, such as experienced at present, starts at around 0700 GMT with stations from the Middle East and both the European and Asian parts of the USSR, with perhaps a few North African stations as well. This reception lasts for about an hour, after which the band is taken over by Western Europeans. Around 1200 GMT the first of the North American stations are audible and they remain in evidence until the band closes. Stations from central and southern Africa and from the Far East may be heard during the late afternoon. In the early evening Caribbean area stations come through followed by South and Central America. The band fades out around 2000 to 2100 GMT.

There are seasonal variations. In the winter months the band will open a little later and may well be closed by 1800 GMT, but from April to September 20 metres may be open until midnight GMT or even later and will be full of stations from the Americas. Late afternoons sometimes produce stations from the western States of the USA and the Canadian Provinces. In the early mornings, shortly after the band opens, Australian and New Zealand stations may be heard together with the west of the USA, Hawaii and the Pacific Islands. Japanese stations are also possible at this time, though by no means assured. Although generally the poorest months, November and December sometimes offer propagation to the islands of the Indian Ocean, such as Reunion and Mayotte, and amateur stations from Antarctic bases are occasionally heard.

At the peak of the sunspot cycle virtually anything is possible. The band is often open right round the clock, unlike the other HF bands, though this is much less likely in the winter than at other times. VK and ZL stations are heard most mornings and this is the very best time to look for Pacific islands which generally have very few amateur radio operators. In past years a net on 14220 kHz (the P29JS net, named after its originator Jim Smith) gave every serious operator first-time reception of several extremely rare countries and many of us went on our way to the office or factory rejoicing!

With such good conditions it is easy to overlook the fact that amateur stations do not operate when they are asleep! Even if reception is theoretically possible there is not normally much point in looking for rare stations which are unlikely to be operating because of the local time in their countries. At 1600 GMT, for example, the time in Fiji is 0400 hours. Lists showing comparative times in each country are not difficult to acquire and the same information is usually shown in atlases. There is, however, always some possibility of logging stations at unusual times during those weekends when major transmitting contests are taking place. Keen contesters will be on the air for as long as they are physically able and can often spring a surprise or two.

Whilst the majority of the QSOs which one hears on 20 metres are in the English language, due in large part to the strong American influence, there is considerable traffic in Spanish, French, German and Russian. The latter two languages are noted especially before noon when European contacts are prevalent. In the evening Spanish is very much to the fore with South and Central American stations talking to each other. French is used by stations in Quebec, Martinique, Guadeloupe and St Pierre & Miquelon Islands, talking to French-speaking European countries. Many of the French QSOs on SSB take place between 14100 and 14120 kHz but this is traditional rather than obligatory since no country has a prescriptive right to any portion of the band to the exclusion of other countries. Spanish-speaking stations from the Americas tend to prefer 14120 to 14200 kHz to avoid much of the QRM from the USA.

21000–21450 kHz (15 metres)

As we get higher in frequency so the effect of the sunspot cycle becomes more pronounced, and this is very evident on the 15 metres amateur band. Scores in excess of 200 countries are attainable during the best years but it can be a hard struggle to reach 150 countries when reception is flat. I heard more than 200 countries in 1979, 1980 and 1981, and three years out of eleven seems par for the course.

The CW portion of 15 metres runs from 21000 to 21150 kHz with telephony occupying the other 300 kilohertz on this large band. USA telephony stations do not transmit below 21200 kHz. When the band is open to the United States most of the DX (for on 15 metres the USA is not considered DX) tries to squeeze into the 21150 to 21200 kHz segment, but one can always hear a fair selection of stations talking to USA operators above 21200 kHz.

At the peak of the sunspot cycle reception is easily possible from all round the world and stations from even the most exotic locations can have very loud signals. The band is rarely open throughout the full twenty-four hours but its closure is sometimes brief, say from 0300 to 0600 GMT. A good day on 21 MHz is sometimes heralded by hordes of Japanese stations at around 0700 GMT; it always seems weird to be logging JA-stations by the dozen without being able to hear any other country whatsoever, but that does happen. As the band drops out to Japan a few other countries from the Far East may be heard, but it is more usual for propagation to switch to Africa. At around 1200 GMT USA and Canadian stations are starting to come through together with the Caribbean islands. The South Americans will show later in the afternoon and the skip will have moved west across the USA to provide stations from California, Oregon, *etc.*

Reception from the USA may then continue until late evening or early morning and the South American stations will probably be the last stations to depart. Even at the best of times 15 metres takes a little while to get into its annual stride; January is invariably a disappointing month and February far from brilliant, but the excitement begins in March when excellent conditions are experienced during the best years.

All this, unfortunately, is a far cry from the minimum sunspot years such as we are experiencing now. There are days when one hears hardly anything on the band but that is no excuse for not listening since conditions vary daily and good openings are there periodically. If there is no propagation to the east — what happened to all those Japanese stations? — a morning session may unearth only a couple of Africans, but they could well be from countries which are difficult to hear on the other bands. Sometimes there will be North American and Caribbean stations in the early afternoon but that is not guaranteed. One can generally find a few South Americans, though, since propagation favours the south during poor conditions. It may seem surprising that European stations are so difficult to hear during the minimum of the sunspot cycle and listeners wanting to increase their scores will make every effort to monitor this band when short-skip conditions are predicted. A good time to listen is during transmitting contests when one can be sure that plenty of stations will be active in the hope of making contacts. During the weekend of the October 1985 CQ Worldwide DX Contest I heard more countries on 15 metres than I had heard in the first nine months of the year!!

African stations have always been fond of 21 MHz and seem to enjoy the best propagation. Even in times of poor reception the Africans are more readily heard on this band than the others. A fair number of them are nationals of European countries who are employed in African countries and endeavour to contact stations in their homeland. British nationals are to be found in countries such as Zambia, Botswana and Malawi (albeit not very many of them), whilst German nationals often transmit from the West African countries and Italians are also represented. A knowledge of the German language is especially useful for listeners to this band when there is propagation from Africa and of course French helps to identify stations from some of the former French colonies. In the afternoons and evenings when South and Central America are being heard the major languages will be Spanish and Portuguese. It is worth emphasizing that conditions can change quickly on 21 MHz and a closed band at 1200 GMT does not necessarily mean that there will be nothing to hear two or three hours later.

28000–29700 kHz (10 metres)

Many amateurs and SWLs swear that this is the most exciting band that we have and it's best not to argue with them! When 10 metres is open listening to it is the most exhilarating experience that amateur radio can offer and can leave even the most experienced listener shaking his head in disbelief. What a pity that it isn't open more often, though one can have too much of a good thing...

The 10 metres band is the largest of our HF bands, stretching for no less than 1700 kHz. European stations use from 28000 to 28200 kHz for CW and from 28200 to 29700 for telephony. The American telephony band starts at 28300 kHz. In practice, few 'phone stations operate below 28400 kHz unless the band is exceptionally crowded but those that do may be undertaking regular schedules and trying to avoid QRM from the DX chasers. The most popular segment of the band is from 28450 to 28650 kHz and one will often not hear stations outside of this range. However, at times of maximum activity stations spread out all over the band and USA stations in particular will be heard well above 29000 kHz.

The sunspot cycle has its greatest effect on 10 metres and the transformation from sunspot minimum to sunspot maximum is truly remarkable. Although the decline is slower it is also very noticeable. My records show the following numbers of countries heard on 10 metres for each year from 1975 to 1985: 60, 58, 114, 176, 201, 196, 214, 192, 157, 114 and 62. In those years of very low scores most of the countries heard were Europeans logged during short-skip conditions plus a few South Americans.

In poor conditions one can monitor the band every day for weeks and not hear a single station. If there is propagation it will generally be from Europe and very selective; one might hear three or four Spanish stations and nobody else, or there could be a brief opening to Brazil which will offer a couple of PY-stations. The major openings to Europe will almost certainly be during the summer months and may last for a couple of hours or so. But when the band is wide open during the best years anything is possible and the simplest antenna will work as efficiently as an expensive one. Transmitting power hardly enters into the calculations as novice stations limited to 30 watts or less will battle it out with stations running much higher

QSL cards received from broadcasting stations (Author's collection).

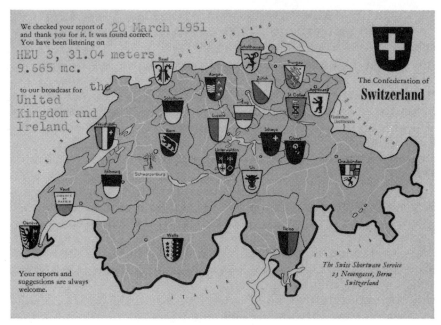

power. Stations from the west coast of the USA and Australians running such low power sound like the BBC and it is best to reduce the receiver's RF gain for maximum intelligibility and less QRM.

Sometimes the conditions on 10 metres are similar to those on 15 metres during the daylight hours as the Japanese stations swamp the band at the start of the day with Australians also strongly in evidence. As time goes by the Africans start to come in, followed by the North Americans and the South Americans. Quite often reception from Russia is very noticeable, with European and Asian Russians being very loud in the mornings and the European stations still being audible throughout the day. It is a good band to check for the rarest Russian oblasts (districts). 10 metres hardly ever remains open much beyond midnight and it therefore appeals to listeners who want to achieve high scores without losing any sleep in the process.

One remarkable feature of the band is that one often hears operators who have been licensed for thirty or forty years and never transmit on any of the other bands. Quite what they do when propagation is non-existent is a mystery. Some of these stations were still using AM until quite recently but an AM signal on 10 metres is now very rare, as it is on all the other bands.

10100–10150 kHz (30 metres), 18068–18168 kHz (16 metres) and 24890–24990 kHz (12 metres)

These are the bands which were allocated to the amateur service at the World Administrative Radio Convention in 1979, but it was some time later before their use was officially authorized. Each of the bands is at present confined to the CW mode in Europe and their potential has not yet been fully exploited. Most of the reports which one sees on these bands relate to 30 metres and they show that DX is fully possible for those stations making the effort. This is not surprising because 30 metres, being midway between 20 and 40 metres, has some of the characteristics of both of those bands. There is, however, a problem with radio teletype (RTTY) transmissions on the band. All continents may be heard and reception in the early hours of the morning is possible. Few stations seem to have ventured onto 16 and 12 metres. At this point in the sunspot cycle the latter band is bound to be unreliable and often completely unusable, but 16 metres should provide some DX when 15 metres is open, mainly from the south.

The reasons for the lack of activity on these bands is no doubt due to the fact that many transmitters available commercially do not have provision for operation on the bands and amateurs are hardly likely to invest in new equipment until propagation conditions improve. Moreover, CW is not everyone's cup of tea and this could deter potential operators. Although there is no blanket embargo worldwide on the use of SSB, transmission of telephony signals is officially discouraged by most amateur radio authorities, if not completely banned as in the United Kingdom.

The Broadcast Bands Explained

Newcomers to short wave radio frequently gain their initial interest by listening to broadcasting stations. There is nothing very surprising about that. Much domestic radio equipment bought for the home has the facility for reception of BC stations. Many owners ignore it completely but the more adventurous, tired of the music and chatter which is the mainstay of many local stations, decide to investigate what foreign stations have to offer. Since BC stations do not transmit in morse code or SSB and use plain language, listeners do not need the type of receiver controls which are necessary for reception of amateurs nor do they require a knowledge of jargon or abbreviations. Their equipment may not be very good but they will certainly hear the most powerful European stations and maybe stations in other continents when conditions are good.

Their interest aroused, they may later decide to invest in a receiver specifically designed for short wave radio. With a suitable aerial this will provide a wider coverage and enable SWLs to become DXers if they so wish. (They will also have the chance of making the acquaintance of amateur radio to add a further dimension to the hobby, of course.) Some listeners will make a point of tuning in regularly to their favourite stations and looking for DX at other times.

Unlike radio amateurs, whose main interest is in communicating with other amateurs, broadcasting stations exist to provide a service to their listeners. Because of this they will do everything possible to ensure that their programmes can be heard and they will welcome suggestions from their audience about programme content and difficulties experienced with reception. Some of them have 'mailbag-type' shows during which listeners' letters are answered; listeners are thereby made to feel that their views really matter (and no doubt they do).

BC stations fall into two distinct categories: domestic broadcasters and international broadcasters. As these terms imply, the domestic stations transmit programmes intended for local audiences in the country of origin whereas the international stations provide programmes of interest to an overseas audience. It is common for countries to transmit both domestic and international broadcasts using different frequencies. The BBC, for instance, has its national Radios 1, 2, 3 and 4 as well as regional stations operating on medium wave, long wave or VHF short wave, whereas the international transmissions are known as the BBC World Service and are mostly (but not exclusively) on HF short wave. This Handbook does not deal with the medium or long waves but there is no doubt that many interesting programmes can be heard on them; DX is certainly a possibility on medium wave though the medium wave DXer will generally need an antenna specifically designed for those frequencies if he is to meet with any great success.

The major international broadcasters such as Radio Moscow, the Voice of America and the BBC (amongst many others) run very high power and obviously use the best equipment available. One has only to pass the site of one of their transmitting stations and look at the array of antennas on display to realize the truth of this statement; if one can obtain permission to go inside the station (which is not often forthcoming) one is astounded by the range of high-quality equipment to be found. A few countries refuse to disclose what powers their stations run but 500 kilowatts is not uncommon these days and powers in excess of that are believed to be used in some instances. When one compares this with the one kilowatt which only the most fortunate amateurs are allowed it will be realized that these 'big boys' of the short wave BC bands really mean business! Domestic stations aiming for a localized area obviously do not need so much power and they may in fact content themselves with the type of power used by amateurs. Many of these stations use no more than ten kilowatts and not a few of them use less than one KW. In these circumstances they must transmit on frequencies where they will not suffer interference from other, higher-powered stations.

Domestic stations are generally on the air for several hours each day and transmit in the language or languages of the country in which they are based. Unless those stations operate around the clock, which is not particularly common, they naturally transmit at times when they are assured of the biggest audience — say from breakfast time to late evening — and it is therefore useful to know the local time in the country concerned. One major variation of this is during the religious festival of Ramadan when stations in Islamic countries often remain on the air for several hours after their usual close-down time. Programmes invariably have a local bias and prominence will be given to local news rather than events in other parts of the world, however important the latter may be. In some cases these radio transmissions will be the only source of news for the population; we tend to forget that there is still a high level of illiteracy in some of the poorer countries and sections of the population may be unable to understand newspapers even if they are available. It must also be remembered that the official language of a country may not necessarily be comprehended by everyone; I recall clearly my efforts to communicate in castilian Spanish with people in the Barcelona region who only spoke catalán and how a bi-lingual castilian/catalán speaker came to my rescue. In the Indian sub-continent there are said to be more than 200 different languages!

International services may use 'domestic-type' languages when broadcasting for the country's citizens abroad but they mostly transmit in languages which are widely spoken throughout the world, especially English, French, Spanish and German. Of course, the intended reception area for the programmes is the governing factor since it would clearly be inappropriate to beam French language transmissions to Australia, for instance. BC bands radio has a strong appeal to those with a penchant for languages and is often used by such people to improve their knowledge of foreign languages. Many radio amateurs gratefully acknowledge that they use the BBC as a means of brushing up their English.

Learning foreign languages does not come easily to everyone but this need not be a serious impediment to listeners aiming to improve their 'country scores' on the broadcast bands. At the commencement of a transmission many stations broadcast a musical interval signal which is associated with the station and soon becomes remembered by listeners. Very often these interval signals (IS) have a particular relevance to the country from which the transmission originates. They may be excerpts from the national anthem but are more likely to be based on musical works by famous composers from the country's past. Listeners to Polish Radio (Radio Polonia), for instance, will have little difficulty in recognizing the *Revolutionary Etude* by Chopin, even if it gives them nightmares trying to play it on the living room piano. The IS is repeated many times before the actual programme begins since it is rarely more than a few seconds

long. From time to time there will be a break whilst the name of the
station is given verbally, generally preceded by the words 'This is . . .'
for English programmes, 'Ici' for French, 'Aquí' for Spanish, 'Hier ist'
for German, 'Huna' for Arabic, 'Govorit' for Russian, *etc*. If the SWL
does not understand anything else he nevertheless stands a good
chance of identifying the station at the start of transmission from
these pointers.

Transmissions by the international broadcasters rarely last for
more than an hour in one language and twenty-five to thirty
minutes is quite common. Following a broadcast in one language
there may be a break of a few minutes, filled by the IS, after which a
programme in another language will begin. These transmissions are
frequently radiated on more than one channel simultaneously to
give listeners with QRM problems the best chance of hearing them.

Callsigns do not play such an important role in broadcast radio as
they do with amateurs. Some countries do not issue them to their
stations, who have to identify themselves as 'Radio . . .' or 'The Voice
of . . .' and so on. Where callsigns are issued the chances are that they
will not be regularly used in transmissions and even if they are they
will often be linked with the station's chosen name. A good example
of this applies to one of the world's best-known stations, which
identifies as 'This is the Voice of the Andes, HCJB, Quito, Ecuador in
South America'.

Where callsigns are given one can identify the country, if
necesarry, by the ITU Block Allocations given in Appendix 1.
Stations which announce themselves as 'Radio . . .' do not always
follow this word with their country for the simple reason that there
may be dozens and dozens of stations in the country all using the
prefix 'Radio', as in the case of Brazil. A good frequency listing is
necessary to identify many of these stations. Similarly, one has to
exercise caution with 'The Voice of . . .' and its equivalents in other
languages ('La Voix de . . .', 'La Voz de . . .', *etc*.). 'The Voice of Nigeria'
is indeed transmitted from Nigeria but there are occasionally
clandestine stations claiming to be 'the voice of' countries where
they are not located and there appear to be numerous stations all
calling themselves 'The Voice of the Revolution'. To a casual listener
it is not always apparent whether these refer to a revolution which
has already taken place or one just about to begin!

Short wave BC stations transmit to published schedules and this is
a great help when it comes to identification. Stations will often send
SWLs copies of their programme bulletins on a 'one-off' or a regular

basis if requested to do so but there is an easier way of obtaining reliable information without the time and expense of writing to stations all over the world and waiting for the replies. *The World Radio TV Handbook*, which celebrated its fortieth anniversary in 1986, provides details of all known broadcasting and television stations on long, medium and short waves, together with programme schedules, frequencies, languages, musical and verbal station identifications, leading personalities, station addresses, *etc*. There are also listings by frequency of long, medium and short wave stations, together with several maps showing transmitter sites, and a number of special articles. The *Handbook*, often known simply as *WRTH*, is an indispensable guide to all serious BC bands listeners and very few would be without it. Published annually by Billboard Publications Inc of New York, the *Handbook* is available in the UK from most booksellers or from the company's agents, Pitman Publishing Ltd, 128 Long Acre, London, WC2E 9AN.

Transmission schedules vary from season to season because of differing propagation conditions. Schedule changes may be expected on the first Sundays in March, May, September and November. In the winter, lower frequencies are often used. In addition to the *WRTH* and its associated publication *WRTH Newsletter* (issued three times per year to update it), clubs specializing in broadcast bands radio usually give details of such changes in their magazines and the DX bulletins transmitted by some broadcasting stations themselves are also a useful source of information. New stations come on the air from time to time and others go QRT. During good conditions stations may be heard which have not been reported for many years.

BC stations are not exempt from the influence of sunspots and the international broadcasters take that factor into account when arranging their schedules. Their concern is to ensure that their programmes reach the desired audiences whatever the propagation conditions, as far as that is possible. During the peak of the sunspot cycle they can be fairly certain that the 21 MHz band will provide a proper service almost all of the time but that is far from being the case at the other end of the cycle. They obviously cannot decide on a day-to-day basis whether to use the band, as radio amateurs can do with their own 21 MHz allocation, and consequently they avoid the band altogether and go for more reliable channels.

As we mentioned earlier, high powers are now the order of the day for many international BC operators yet very many other stations transmitting only domestic services use minimal power. If all of these stations were to congregate on the same frequency ranges the effect would be totally predictable. For this reason certain frequency bands are allocated only to domestic stations in the tropical regions and these are understandably popular with keen DXers. The bands in question are 60, 90 and 120 metres and it is here that Indonesian, African and Latin American stations are to be found unmolested by the high-power brigade. The best reception is in autumn, winter and early spring when QRN is at its lowest. Few of the stations broadcast in English, with the exception of those African countries with strong ties with Britain, such as Kenya and Tanzania.

Having read the preceding chapter about the characteristics of the amateur bands, readers will have a general idea of what to expect on the BC bands in the way of propagation. The 19 metres band, for instance, will have much in common in this respect with the 20 metres amateur band. In reality things may be a little different; whereas amateurs are all restricted to comparatively low power and can compete with each other on equal terms, low-powered BC stations have no desire to battle it out with the 'megastations' (to coin a word) which have taken up residence there and they will seek quieter pastures. It is now time, therefore, to look at what each of the standard BC bands has to offer.

2300–2498 kHz (120 metres)

This is the lowest of the BC frequencies and is not widely used. Most of the stations to be found here are from Indonesia, though there are a few South and Central Americans. Powers used are mainly of the order of one kilowatt and it takes great perseverance and good equipment to do well on this band.

3200–3400 kHz (90 metres)

The European winter is the best time to look for DX on 90 metres, with December to February being the recommended months. The best years are likely to be when the sunspot count is low. The Far East, South America and Africa provide most of the stations which are mainly low-powered though one or two use up to 100 KW. The central and southern African stations run the highest power: look for South Africa on 3250 and 3320 kHz, Zambia on 3346, Malawi on 3380 and Zimbabwe on 3396 kHz.

3900–4000 kHz (75 metres)

These frequencies are used by radio amateurs in the western hemisphere and the BC stations to be found here are mainly from Asia and Africa, though some European stations such as Swiss Radio International and the BBC use QRGs at the top end of the band. The most powerful stations are from South Africa, Namibia, Switzerland, the Voice of America relay in Liberia, and the BBC stations in Great Britain and Cyprus. The best time to listen for DX on this band is during the winter months (preferably around sunspot minimum years) during the late afternoon and evenings. Since USA radio amateurs provide great competition overnight when conditions are good, hearing the low-powered BC stations at these times can be very difficult indeed. Reception during the summer months is often awkward because of static.

4750–5060 kHz (60 metres)

120, 90 and 60 metres are known as 'tropical bands' because they are allocated by the ITU for use only in tropical areas. Of the three, 60 metres is unquestionably the most popular and enjoys something approaching cult status with many listeners. Whereas long antennas are most beneficial on the other two bands, good results can be obtained on 60 metres with aerials which also perform well on the higher frequencies and QRN, although certainly a problem on this band during the summer months, is not so severe as on 90 metres. Since the high-powered international broadcasters do not use the band the DX stations stand a much better chance of being heard in Europe than higher up the spectrum. This can be a good 'day and night' band with African stations being heard in the late afternoon and evening periods and South and Central Americans in the overnight periods.

The World Radio TV Handbook lists all the known stations using this band (as it does for the other bands) and the following stations, taken from this source, are worthy of investigation:

4750 kHz R. Bertoua, Cameroon
4760 kHz Trans World Radio, Swaziland
4764 kHz R.R.I. Medan, Indonesia
4770 kHz Kaduna, Nigeria
4777 kHz Libreville, Gabon
4785 kHz Dar es Salaam, Tanzania
4795 kHz R. Douala, Cameroon

4804 kHz Nairobi, Kenya
4815 kHz Ouagadougou, Burkina Faso
4820 kHz Gaberone, Botswana
4830 kHz Africa No. 1, Gabon
4835 kHz Bamako, Mali
4840 kHz Koma Rock, Kenya
4845 kHz Nouakchott, Mauritania
4845 kHz R. Nacional Manaus, Brazil
4850 kHz Yaoundé, Cameroon
4870 kHz Cotonou, Benin
4885 kHz Nairobi, Kenya
4890 kHz Dakar, Senegal
4910 kHz Lusaka, Zambia
4915 kHz Nairobi, Kenya
4925 kHz Batá, Equatorial Guinea
4930 kHz Windhoek, Namibia
4940 kHz Abidjan, Ivory Coast
4960 kHz N'djamena, Chad
4980 kHz R. Ecos del Torbes, Venezuela
5004 kHz Batá, Equatorial Guinea
5005 kHz Khumaltar, Nepal
5010 kHz R. Garoua, Cameroon
5020 kHz Niamey, Niger
5027 kHz Kampala, Uganda
5055 kHz Trans World Radio, Swaziland

Many of these stations are regularly reported in Europe during the winter months. By and large the South and Central American stations, which are also very active on the band, use lower powers than the Africans and are not heard so regularly (apart from a selection in Brazil and Venezuela), but there is tremendous variety: in the winter of 1986, for instance, such stations as R. Nueva America, Bolivia, 4797 kHz (1 KW); La Voz Evangelica, Honduras, 4820 kHz (5 KW); R. Reloj, Costa Rica, 4832 kHz (3 KW); and R. Tazulutlán, Guatemala, 4835 kHz (5 KW) were being reported. 60 metres is also a good band to use for listening to the domestic service programmes from China and the Far Eastern zone of the USSR. It is hardly surprising that 60 metres is so popular with serious DXers.

5950–6200 kHz (49 metres)

This band is one of the most heavily populated BC bands and is justifiably highly regarded by listeners. Here one finds low-powered Latin Americans fighting it out with the major international broadcasters and whilst it is not easy to find DX there is always a possibility of rare catches, especially during the early hours of the day when the skip favours long-distance reception and the European stations may well be QRT. Because 49 metres is not greatly affected by the sunspot cycle it is always busy, especially during periods of low sunspot activity when its regular population is joined by other stations moving down from higher frequencies. Reception of stations around the clock is more likely here than on most of the other bands and newcomers to the hobby will find 49 metres a good place to begin. During the present phase of the sunspot cycle the hours of darkness in winter are most likely to produce the DX catches which make short wave listening so interesting. Daytime reception is often confined to European stations.

7100–7300 kHz (41 metres)

As in the case of the 75 metres band, 41 metres is used in the western hemisphere by amateur radio stations and the BC stations do not operate from there. This is another very widely used band which has similarities with 49 metres in that propagation is generally reliable at all times and stations can be heard at all hours of the day and night. Despite the large number of stations active, logging of DX is not easy because of the high powers used by the Europeans and it is perhaps fair to say that 41 metres has less followers than the other bands which provide as much activity.

Listeners in Europe may be forgiven for thinking that the band actually covers the whole frequency range from 7000 to 7300 kHz because there are several stations which operate in the European portion of the 40 metres amateur band (7000 to 7100 kHz). As we have already seen, the International Telecommunications Union regulates the radio spectrum and allocates frequencies for the various radio services. However, some countries choose to ignore the ITU recommendations.

9500–9775 kHz (31 metres)

The 31, 25 and 19 metres bands have much in common with each other. They are all dominated by the international broadcasters running high power and several stations transmit programmes on all three bands simultaneously. At times of high sunspot activity there is not a lot to choose between them but in poorer conditions, when the maximum usable frequency (MUF) is lower, 31 metres is likely to be the pick of the bunch. If one had to recommend a particular band for a complete newcomer to the BC bands, this would probably be the one.

In good years 31 metres will usually be open around the clock, except perhaps in mid-winter when it sometimes closes briefly in the early hours. In other years it will often be open when 25 and 19 metres have folded up for the day. Reception during the daytime is mainly of European stations but the hours of darkness during spring, summer and autumn will sometimes provide very long-distance reception over several thousand miles. The best time to listen for DX, as on so many other bands, is around sunrise and sunset times. In addition to the powerful stations there is a sprinkling of low-powered South Americans on this band which are always worth chasing.

11700–11975 kHz (25 metres)
As we move higher in frequency the effects of the sunspot cycle become more noticeable during the poorer years. Whilst this band provides reliable world-wide communications at all times when the sunspots are running in its favour it is rather more erratic on other occasions. Nevertheless it does have much to commend it compared with the higher frequencies. The problem here is to try and separate the stations on the dial, for most of the broadcasters on 25 metres seem to be running 500 kilowatts! The low-powered stations tend to keep off the band for obvious reasons. With so many stations having deserted their higher QRGs because of the unreliable propagation during the sunspot minimum there are now so many broadcasters on 11 MHz that levels of interference are often intense. Here again, monitoring the band around sunrise is recommended for DX stations and late afternoons in spring and early autumn are also worthwhile with possibilities of reception from the Far East.

15100–15450 kHz (19 metres)
This is another band colonized by the international broadcasting stations. All continents are represented, with many stations using from 50 to 500 KW. During sunspot maxima this band provides reliable communications throughout the year but the trans-formation at the other end of the cycle is very pronounced. Daytime reception of relatively local stations is usually assured but the band may well fade out before the DX has a chance of showing up. In the

winter months 19 metres may close as early as 1700 GMT and not reopen until sunrise the next day. Autumn will often see the band closing mid-evening. The best times to listen during these conditions (which should however begin to improve around the year 1989) are during the spring and late summer, when the band will often be open after midnight. There is bound to be a great deal of QRM on this band at the present time because of the immigrants displaced from the higher frequencies.

17700–17900 kHz (16 metres)

This band also has an interesting range of stations from throughout the world and all continents may be heard. 'European domination' is not so strong as on other bands and listening to 16 metres can be very rewarding. Even in the best of conditions the band is not normally regarded as a '24 hours' operation and in times of mediocre conditions it is best to listen primarily in the daytime when stations in excess of 1,500 miles (2,400 km) are most likely to be heard without a great deal of interference from European stations, except perhaps during the 'short skip' conditions sometimes experienced in summer. The best times to listen are from autumn to spring since summertime reception tends to be poor.

21450–21750 kHz (13 metres)

The 13 metres broadcasting band starts where the 21 MHz amateur band finishes and listeners with ostensibly 'amateur bands only' receivers have a chance of hearing a few BC stations in some instances. Not surprisingly, the band is very much affected by the sunspot cycle and reliable reception during sunspot minima is far from assured; on many occasions the band may be closed completely. BC stations often move away from 13 metres at these times and the most probable time for decent reception is during daylight hours. Europe, Asia and Africa are the continents mainly represented and there is very little to hear from elsewhere. Late autumn to early spring tends to produce the best conditions, though high-powered Africans can often be heard during the summer.

25600–26100 kHz (11 metres)

At times of high solar activity almost anything is possible on this band, just as it is on the 10 metres amateur band, but the story is totally different when sunspots are absent. Few international broadcasters will endeavour to use 11 metres on these latter occasions and there will be many times when the band is completely closed, sometimes for weeks at a time. Keen DXers will nevertheless keep a check on the band, especially in summer when unusual propagation conditions sometimes arise. The most likely DX path is north-to-south and reception of stations from the east and west would be most unusual. The best conditions will normally be in autumn and spring but the absence of stations using the band may well negate any benefits of this.

Unlike radio amateurs, who have to keep within the officially authorized bands, broadcasting stations are very often found outside of the frequency ranges just described. There is therefore a strong case for monitoring the entire short wave spectrum whilst concentrating on the recognized bands for most of the time. The frequencies immediately above and below the standard bands are likely to be the most interesting, for stations who set up shop 'miles from anywhere' are mainly from the USSR, China, Albania and other countries which are easy to hear on the other frequency ranges.

The World Administrative Radio Conference in 1979, already mentioned in connection with the amateur bands, agreed to create new broadcasting frequencies by 'adding on' segments to existing bands. These new frequencies were to be: 9775–9900 kHz; 11650–11700 kHz; 11975–12050 kHz; 15450–15600 kHz; 17550–17700 kHz; and 21750–21850 kHz. Although it was not intended that these additional frequencies should be used pending further investigations (which were not complete at the time of writing), a number of stations have already started using them and it is therefore advisable to monitor them fairly regularly. The type of propagation to be expected will be similar to that of the band to which they are added.

Although stations generally operate on known frequencies, whether officially recognized or not, they can and do change channels from time to time either to take advantage of changing propagation conditions or to avoid QRM from adjacent stations. There is also a third possible reason — transmitter instability! Many domestic broadcasters are not well blessed with funds and have to make do with equipment which would be viewed with derision by their better-heeled brethren. At the same time their 'technical staff' may be only one person who might be out of his depth in trying to investigate any serious problem which may arise. For this reason it is not unknown for stations to transmit slightly higher or lower in frequency than their allocated channels, and instances are sometimes reported where stations actually drift in QRG whilst programmes are being transmitted! When looking for a low-powered station on a particular frequency, therefore, listeners should not jump too readily to the conclusion that they are hearing the station they want because they have found the allocated channel and there is a station broadcasting on it. Before accepting that one has genuinely heard a wanted station it is important that a proper verbal or musical identification is heard by the SWL.

The types of programme transmitted by the stations vary with the intended audience. A typical broadcast from an international broadcaster will contain international news, local news considered of interest to overseas listeners, a short talk on a current affairs subject, musical interludes, information about the station's country (often with a view to encouraging tourism), interviews with visiting VIPs, *etc.* The broadcast will quote the frequencies on which the station is transmitting and will terminate with information about forthcoming transmissions. Stations which welcome letters and reception reports from listeners will give their postal address. This format is widely used but is adapted by some countries, most notably in Eastern Europe, to ensure that the programmes have a strong political bias. Stations which transmit fairly lengthy shows may also include plays, classical music, *etc.*

Domestic broadcasters obviously gear their programmes to matters of particular interest to the local inhabitants of the area their transmissions are intended to cover. Because they transmit for several hours every day they are naturally able to cover the whole range of types of programme, from pop music to serious drama and with all kinds of information in between. These schedules can be compared with the style of programming used by BBC Radios 2 and 4 on our own medium and long waves. It could even be that some of the shows were originally heard on the BBC stations, for the BBC, in common with other broadcasting networks, makes use of its Transcription Service to provide overseas stations with copies of its most interesting programmes or most popular comedy shows. This, of course, is a pitfall for the unwary, who may understandably assume that re-runs of 'The Goon Show' must automatically be coming from London. Domestic stations identify themselves periodically for the benefit of listeners but not always with the clarity that one gets from the 'internationals', and one sometimes has to listen most carefully over a long period before being certain that one's identification of a station is correct.

Very many of the smaller stations depend for their existence on a high level of advertizing and this is strongly reflected in the programmes. The British 'natural break' style of advertizing is not widely used and it is more common for adverts to be slotted into the programmes at every opportunity, whatever effect this creates. Latin American stations use advertizing to a considerable extent and their geographical area can often be determined by the style of the adverts, including the mention of particular currencies. To a listener unaccustomed to this style of presentation it can be either irritating or comical, depending on one's mood at the time. Whilst in Peru some years ago I listened to a sports commentary which managed to include a reference to 'Coca cola, la chispa de la vida' virtually once every minute and sometimes twice per minute!

Revolutions and *coups d'état* occur in countries from time to time — readers may be thinking that this chapter is obsessed with revolutions! — and one of the first actions of any potential new government is to seize control of the country's main radio network. Occasionally, therefore, listeners may have the chance of hearing history in the making if they happen to be monitoring the bands at the right time. After all, this is how news is obtained by the BBC and other stations for transmission in their own programmes. Whenever such an event becomes known, therefore, it is useful to check the frequencies used by stations in the country concerned for first-hand information. This facility is not available to amateur bands listeners because of the embargo on the discussion of politics and is no doubt one of the most exciting aspects of broadcast radio.

Deliberate QRM in the form of jamming of stations is unfortunately widespread on the BC bands. It is difficult to describe the sound of this but once heard it is never forgotten. The noise creates a blanket which wipes out reception over a range of several kilohertz and is intended to prevent listeners hearing stations considered objectionable to the station causing the noise. Sometimes the stations being obliterated are clandestine operations which should not be on the bands anyway but they are more often legitimate stations from countries currently at loggerheads with other countries. This type of interference is most prevalent at times of international tension but there are always examples to be found whatever the general state of world affairs.

The term 'clandestine stations' is usually reserved for broadcasters who transmit programmes of a political nature opposed to the governments of certain countries. They tend to use slogans like 'The Voice of Free . . .' and attempt to create anti-government feeling in the areas to which their transmissions are directed. Since the programmes are aimed at the local population they are normally, but not invariably, in the language of the area concerned, which is not necessarily the language of the country as a whole. Because these stations would certainly be closed down by the governments of the countries affected if their locations could be detected, it is not unusual for these 'pirate' broadcasters to move around, though they generally remain on the same frequencies unless they are being jammed. Stations may claim to be transmitting from a particular country but this is rarely guaranteed; a station opposed to the South African government, for instance, is more likely to be in a neighbouring country than in South Africa itself.

The so-called 'pop pirates' which some of us came to know and love in the sixties have mostly ceased operations, but there are still a few which transmit their programmes of pop music and advertizing from vessels anchored in international waters. Reception of most, if not all, of these stations is not permitted by UK regulations.

As a service to their listeners, some stations transmit bulletins of information dedicated to DXers and these are always worth hearing as the news is more current than that often found in magazines. At least, it ought to be, though the odd instance has been observed of stations extracting their news from the aforementioned magazines literally word for word! It is always dangerous to attempt to give precise information about particular broadcasts in a book of this type since schedules change with such regularity. As a general guide, though, Appendix 9 lists those stations which do have DX bulletins in English with the times of transmissions. This information has been extracted from *World Radio TV Handbook* and is the latest available at the time of writing. Whereas DX bulletins transmitted by BC stations formerly used to confine themselves to the broadcast bands, there is now a tendency for information about the amateur bands and other aspects of electronics to be included in some of them.

We have already considered the possibility of confusion in locating the bases used by clandestine stations. A similar difficulty arises in the case of some international broadcasters (who may object to being included in the same paragraph, though no disrespect is intended!) who use relay sites to provide a greater geographical coverage of their programmes. Stations such as the BBC, The Voice of America, Radio Nederland, Deutsche Welle and one or two others have relay stations which allow them to reach their intended catchment areas with more reliability than would be achieved if all of their programmes had to reach the listeners direct. Since SWLs who keep a score of countries heard need to count countries based on transmitter sites, it follows that they must know whether they are listening to a direct transmission from the originating country or a relayed transmission from another country. The stations themselves are not always helpful in this respect and it is very easy to hear a relay station without realizing it. Here again, *WRTH* often comes to the rescue but if there is any doubt it might be beneficial to write to the station and ask. The relay stations have been instrumental in making available to listeners countries which were very difficult to hear before their establishment and they are to be welcomed for that.

Relay stations which are worth checking out are used by the following major international broadcasters:

British Broadcasting Corporation: Berlin, West Germany; Ascension Island; Lesotho; Cyprus; Masirah Island, Oman; Singapore; Sackville, Canada; Delano and Greenville, USA; Antigua.

Voice of America: Ascension Island; Antigua; Belize; Botswana; Brazil; Colombo, Sri Lanka; Costa Rica; Kavala, Greece; Monrovia, Liberia; Munich, West Germany; Philippines; Rhodes, Dodecanese Islands; Tangier, Morocco; Thailand; Woofferton, England.

Radio Nederland: Bonaire, Netherlands Antilles (Windward group); Talata/Volonodry, Madagascar.

Deutsche Welle: Kigali, Rwanda; Sines, Portugal; Malta; Antigua; Montserrat; Trincomalee, Sri Lanka; Canada.

It will be readily seen what an important part these relay stations play in providing opportunities for listeners to improve their country scores.

Religion is the *raison d'être* of several stations to be found on the broadcasting bands and there is no shortage of denominations catered for. Possibly the biggest two names in religious broadcasting are Trans World Radio and the Far East Broadcasting Company Inc, known by the initials TWR and FEBC respectively. Trans World Radio has transmitting facilities in Monte Carlo, Monaco (where it is based); Bonaire; Swaziland; Guam; Cyprus; Sri Lanka; and Uruguay. As its name implies, the Far East Broadcasting Co is firmly rooted in the east and its transmitters are to be found in the Philippines (where it has many sites); Korea; Saipan in the Marianas Islands; the Seychelles; and San Francisco in the USA. One feature of the religious broadcasting services is that the same transmitting station may well be used to radiate the programmes of several different religious organizations. These stations are almost invariably funded by donations.

To conclude this chapter, let us take the example of Swiss Radio International to give some details of a large, well-known and popular broadcasting station.

The Swiss Shortwave Service made its first experimental broadcasts to the Americas in 1934 and in 1935 regular short wave broadcasts began in German, French and Italian using a transmitter at Prangins in Western Switzerland belonging to the League of Nations. The first Swiss short wave transmitter went into service at Schwarzenburg, near Berne, in 1939. Regular broadcasts in English, Spanish and Portuguese began in 1941 and Esperanto was added in 1946, when transmitter power was increased from 25 to 100 kilowatts.

In 1962 the Swiss Shortwave Service was recognized as a separate organization within the framework of the Swiss Broadcasting Corporation and introduced the first international news service in Switzerland. Programmes in Arabic were introduced in 1964 and Romansch was added in 1971.

Transmitter power was also increased in stages and in 1972 it reached 500 KW with a new transmitter near Sottens in Western Switzerland. The rotating antenna at this site was the most modern in the world. Swiss Broadcasting Corporation took over all the costs of running the services in 1977 when the Confederation withdrew the financial contribution it had made since 1963 and in the following year the Swiss Shortwave Service became known as Swiss Radio International.

The two-fold task of Swiss Radio International, stated in the charter granted to it by the Swiss Government, is to strengthen the ties between Swiss living abroad and their native country as well as to promote Switzerland's image around the world. To carry out this mandate Swiss Radio International maintains a daily twenty-four-hour schedule of short wave programmes which are beamed world-wide.

Swiss Radio International employs a staff of approximately 130 people including many non-Swiss broadcasters and journalists who prepare and present the foreign language programmes. Each day,

Headquarters of SRI (Swiss Radio International).

except Sunday, there is a current affairs radio magazine reflecting developments in Switzerland and abroad. In addition to news bulletins these programmes include commentaries, reviews of the Swiss press, interviews and special reports. On Sundays there are cultural, documentary and entertainment programmes. Every effort is made to present all programmes in a clear, balanced and comprehensive way. The central newsroom compiles some fifty news bulletins per day from information provided by major agencies and correspondents and all information is double-checked before it is broadcast to ensure accuracy.

Left *SRI's rotating antenna near Sottens* (Swiss Radio International).
Above *Modern equipment located in the studios in Berne* (Swiss Radio International).

The programmes are transmitted from several centres in Switzerland; at Schwarzenburg there are four transmitters with a power of 250 KW each and two with 100 KW; at Sottens there is one transmitter of 500 KW; at Lenk (Bernese Oberland) there are two 250 KW transmitters; Sarnen (Central Switzerland) has one 250 KW TX and Beromunster (Central Switzerland) serves as a reserve centre with two stand-by transmitters of 250 KW.

Swiss Radio International has a transcription service for radio stations abroad, inaugurated in 1972, which has been put at the disposal of more than 500 radio organizations throughout the world.

The programme schedule of Swiss Radio International changes in May and November each year. The November 1986 schedule showed transmissions to Europe on 3985 kHz from 0700 to 1200 and 1430 to 2400, on 6165 kHz from 0700 to 2400, on 9535 kHz from 0700 to 1800 and on 12030 kHz from 1200 to 1430. (In the earlier summer schedule 9535 kHz was used until 2400 GMT.)

English was scheduled for 0830 to 0900, 1400 to 1430, 1900 to 1930 and 2330 to 2400 GMT. Services to other continents used 5965, 6135, 9560, 9625, 9665, 9670, 9725, 9730, 9870, 9885, 11795, 11840, 11935, 12035, 15430 and 15570 kHz and, of course, many of these transmissions will also be heard in Europe.

The English programmes feature 'Dateline' (news and current affairs) from Monday to Saturday, and on Saturday the 'Swiss Shortwave Merry-go-round' is also broadcast. 'The Grapevine' is featured on the first and third Sundays and 'Supplement' on the second and fourth Sundays.

Swiss Radio International welcomes letters from listeners and these should be addressed to SRI at CH-3000 Berne 15, Switzerland.

Lists of frequencies used by a selection of major international broadcasting stations are given in Appendix 10.

The VHF and UHF Bands

First there were low frequencies, then there were high frequencies, next came very high frequencies and now we have ultra high frequencies... The science of radio has come a long way in the past few decades. If Marconi were alive today he would probably be amazed to find not only that the medium waveband on which he made his original broadcasts is still in use but also that experiments are being made with QRGs as high as 2000 MHz (or two GigaHertz, 2 GHz).

In the pioneering days of radio it was generally thought that what we now call the short waves were of use to neither man nor beast. Perhaps the beasts were inclined to agree but once radio amateurs had been banished to there from the long and medium waves, which were filling up with broadcasting stations, the men were in for a revelation. Far from being useless it was found that the short waves were much better for long-distance communication, thanks to the effects of ionospheric propagation.

The BC stations were soon to take advantage of the short wave HF bands and shared them with the amateurs, who had their own segments allotted to them. But what of frequencies higher than 30 MHz? Who was going to exploit *them*?

The answer, not very surprisingly, was the amateurs, who had been responsible for most of the progress already made in radio. They still retained their HF allocations but were also allowed the use of the 144 MHz VHF band and the 432 MHz UHF band. Since there was virtually no equipment commercially available for these bands the amateurs naturally constructed their own and set about experimenting. After all, experimentation had long been the name of the game.

At that time — more than thirty years ago now — almost all countries had only one class of amateur radio licence. The early VHF transmitting stations had often learnt their skills on the HF bands and were seeking new challenges. One read periodically in the radio press of new records being set for long-distance working as the peculiar properties of the VHF bands were exploited.

Because of the lack of equipment few SWLs joined in the research on the band above 30 MHz, but when it became evident that VHF/UHF propagation was more interesting than had generally been realized some of the more experienced listeners built converters which could be used with their communications receivers covering the HF bands, and in due course such converters became available commercially. Those listeners (and of course amateurs) who lived in well-populated areas were the most successful because they were able to hear local amateurs regularly, but other SWLs sometimes went for days without hearing anyone at all.

VHF radio really came into its own when several countries, including Great Britain, introduced a 'junior' class of licence which allowed use of the VHF/UHF bands by enthusiasts who had not passed the CW examination but had the necessary technical qualifications for an amateur transmitting licence. Some amateurs went on to VHF/UHF whilst still seeking to obtain proficiency in morse which would allow them to obtain full licences and operate on all the amateur bands; others were quite content to remain on VHF/UHF.

Once VHF propagation had been researched by the amateurs the broadcast stations, not to be outdone, decided to get in on the act. Because of the short distances over which VHF signals travel in normal circumstances the BC stations were able to transmit to their intended audiences with little QRM from other stations, and many of them used the opportunity to develop broadcasting in FM stereo, creating a new dimension in radio transmission which has been widely appreciated by their listeners.

Despite all this activity it is probably true to say that there are comparatively few SWLs who listen to these bands compared with those who monitor the HF bands. (We exclude here, of course, those who merely listen to their local BBC and commercial radio stations and who would not regard themselves as Short Wave Listeners any more than commuters who go to work by train would call themselves railway enthusiasts.) The reason for this is not difficult to understand: compared with the HF bands reception, even at the best of times, covers shorter distances and it is usually considered more exciting to hear Radio Australia than, say, Swiss Broadcasting

Corporation even if, technically, the latter may be a rarer catch.

Several books are now available dealing with VHF and UHF radio and it is indeed a most interesting aspect of the hobby. (Incidentally, the ultra high frequencies are regarded as starting at 300 MHz and frequencies above 1 GHz are also known as 'microwaves'.) At the same time, equipment is now widely available in the form of specialized RXs and TXs (and, more often, transceivers) as well as antennas. The fact remains, though, that newcomers to short wave radio will not normally start on the VHF/UHF bands unless their initial interest was acquired from amateurs active on those bands, and this chapter deliberately avoids going into considerable detail for that reason.

Where are the VHF and UHF bands? The VHF BC bands extend from 66 to 72 MHz in Eastern Europe and from 87 to 108 MHz elsewhere. They are also used by some 'utility' services such as police transmissions. UHF is not used by broadcasting stations because its normal reception distance is far too short. There are several amateur bands, of which the only ones in regular use in the UK are as follows:

70.025 to 70.7 MHz (4 metres)
144.0 to 146.0 MHz (2 metres)
432.0 to 440.0 MHz (70 centimetres)
1215.0 to 1325.0 MHz (23 centimetres)

In addition to CW, transmissions on AM, SSB, FM and DSB (double sideband) are allowed on some of these bands as well as amateur television transmissions.

The 50 to 54 MHz (6 metres) band has been used in North America for many years and is particularly useful during periods of high sunspot activity when DX propagation is regularly possible. This band has just been made available in Great Britain on an experimental basis and contacts between here and the USA will be expected as the next sunspot peak approaches.

Many modern receivers, including inexpensive ones, allow reception of local stations on the VHF BC bands though they are not much use for DX listening. For the best BC reception one needs a more sophisticated RX with a proper VHF antenna, the latter readily available on the market or via aerial erectors who advertize their services in the newspapers.

In the chapter on Receivers and antennas we considered new RXs currently available and some of these are also supplied with VHF converters where required. This applies in the cases of the Trio

R2000, Yaesu FRG-8800 and Japan Radio Company NRD-525 and anyone purchasing those receivers would be advised to consider buying the associated converters at the same time. There are, however, RXs specifically designed for VHF and UHF and details of a selection of these are given below.

Icom IC-R7000

Coverage from 25 to 1000 MHz and 1025 to 2000 MHz, including the 28 MHz amateur band and the VHF BC bands. Modes: FM wide, FM narrow, AM, SSB (USB/LSB). Ninety-nine programmable memories. Scanning system. Digital QRG readout to 100 Hz. Six tuning speeds. Dial lock, noise blanker, combined 'S'-meter and centre meter. Power: 117/220/234v AC. Audio output 2.5 watts. Optional remote controller unit and speech synthesizer unit at extra cost.
Price (mid-1987): £832 + VAT.
Distributor: ICOM (UK) Ltd, Unit 9, Sea Street, Herne Bay, Kent, CT6 8LD.

Yaesu FRG-9600

Coverage from 60 MHz to 905 MHz. Modes: FM narrow, FM wide, AM narrow, AM wide, SSB (to 460 MHz). 100 programmable memory channels. Scanning facility. Seven tuning speeds. One watt audio output. Power: 100/117/220–230v AC and 12–15v DC. Digital readout to 100 Hz. 24-hour clock/timer. Recorder output socket. 'S'-meter. May be used with personal computers for additional control functions via CAT Interface Units.
Price (Spring 1987): £478.26 + VAT.
Distributor: South Midlands Communications Ltd, S.M. House, School Close, Chandlers Ford Industrial Estate, Eastleigh, Hampshire, SO5 3BY.

A.O.R. AR2002

Coverage from 25 to 550 MHz and 800 to 1300 MHz, including 28 MHz amateur band and 87 to 108 MHz BC band. Modes: AM, FM wide, FM narrow. Three tuning speeds. Twenty memory channels storing QRG and mode information, recalled manually or via automatic scanning. General scanning facility. Digital readout to 100 Hz. Clock. Power: 12–14v DC (suitable 230v/12v power supply included); battery operation possible for mobile operation. Range of

Above *Icom IC-R7000 VHF/UHF receiver* (Icom (UK) Ltd).

Below *Yaesu FRG-9600 VHF/UHF receiver* (South Midlands Communications Ltd).

suitable antennas available for mobile and fixed station working.
Price (mid-1987): £423.50 + VAT.
Distributor: Lowe Electronics Ltd, Chesterfield Road, Matlock,
Derbyshire, DE4 5LE.

Those who cannot or do not want to afford new equipment may
be able to obtain VHF/UHF receivers second-hand. Many people,
however, prefer to buy converters which can be used with their HF
receivers; these generally cover only one amateur band but that is
not such a handicap as it sounds since listeners often like to
specialize. Microwave Modules Ltd manufacture a good range of
converters which are extremely popular and worthy of serious
consideration. A useful source of information on what is available
are the advertisement pages of the monthly magazines obtainable on
news-stands.

When it comes to antennas, the simple length of wire which often
suffices for the HF bands is not suitable and it is essential to use a
specialized VHF antenna. Many types are available and, here again,
details can be found in magazines. These antennas are fairly small
and usually attached to a chimney; they take up little room and are
not regarded as eyesores by neighbours.

South Midlands Communications Ltd market a VHFL Skeleton
Discone Antenna for reception of 65 to 520 MHz, which is
omnidirectional. This is illustrated, as is the LT606 Log Periodic
Antenna for 50 to 500 MHz, which is also used for transmitting.

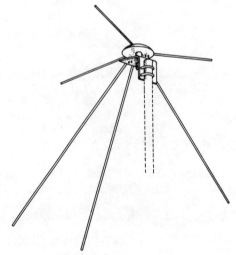

VHFL skeleton discone antenna (SMC Ltd).

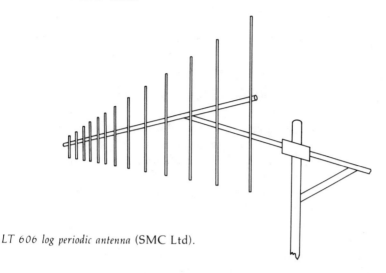

LT 606 log periodic antenna (SMC Ltd).

Jaybeam Ltd manufacture numerous VHF antennas for specific amateur bands which are much used by amateur stations. Lowe Electronics Ltd retail these antennas and will provide information. For listeners who want to monitor a wide range of frequencies, Lowe recommend the Revco REVCONE Model 2050, as illustrated below, which has full VHF and UHF coverage.

It is always worth bearing in mind that many amateurs are now

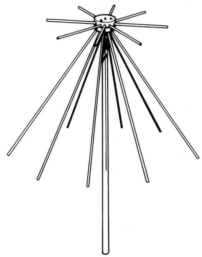

Revco Model 2050 antenna (Lowe Electronics Ltd).

concentrating on the VHF/UHF bands and will have had experience of several types of antenna. Amateurs are a friendly crowd and are always willing to assist newcomers with helpful advice. If readers are able to get to a local radio club and ask a few questions they will find their time well spent.

In normal circumstances, propagation above 30 MHz is based on line-of-sight distance, taking into account the curvature of the earth. This doesn't mean that one actually has to be able to see the other station before contact can be made, of course, since very few QSOs would take place if that were so! What it does mean is that there must be no obstacles such as hills between the two stations and it therefore follows that those stations located at a high altitude are more likely to be successful than others. Quite obviously the height of a station's transmitting antenna above ground is also important and the higher it is the better.

To assist stations who are not favourably placed geographically there are several amateur radio repeater stations which are strategically placed at high altitudes and receive and re-transmit signals from one amateur operator to another. These repeaters, as they are called, allow contacts which would not otherwise be made and are frequently used not only by fixed stations but also by mobile operators.

The most fascinating part of VHF/UHF radio is when unusual propagation conditions occur and the normal line-of-sight rules are suspended. In these instances reception over long distances is possible and stations in the British Isles may have contacts with stations on the European mainland and maybe even North Africa. These conditions can occur with little warning and may last from just a few minutes to a couple of days. The most likely time can sometimes be predicted and it is worth studying current radio magazines for details.

The most common of these interesting propagation possibilities is known as Sporadic-E. Signals are carried into the ionosphere and are reflected by the E-layer, which is about 60 to 80 miles (96–128 km) above the earth. Contacts over distances of more than 1,000 miles (1,600 km) are possible when these conditions prevail on the 70 and 144 MHz bands, though this is not such a great help on 70 MHz as it is on the other band since very few European countries have the use of 70 MHz. Tropospheric ducting ('tropo') is another form of long-distance communication and this is most likely to occur during fine, warm, settled weather at low altitudes, though tropospheric ducting does sometimes occur in winter during settled weather with the barometer just beginning to drop. These conditions, which considerably extend the normal range for communications, affect not only the 70 and 144 MHz bands but can also reach as high as the UHF bands.

Reflections from aurora in the polar regions also provide an interesting variation. When these conditions exist stations transmit to and receive signals from the north regardless of the actual location of the station which they are working. Auroral reflection, which can sometimes affect the HF bands also, can often be recognized from the fluttery quality of the signals and it is far easier for contacts to be made on CW than on telephony. Other, less frequent, types of contact over long distances can be due to 'meteor scatter' (when meteors collide with the upper atmosphere and create brief ionization) and signals bounced off the moon. It goes without saying that contacts of this latter type are extremely rare.

Readers may well feel that interesting long-distance VHF and UHF propagation is akin to a lottery. Certainly there is not the reliability that one finds on the HF bands — and, to be honest, the HF bands during periods of low sunspot activity are not always reliable themselves. The most successful VHF listeners will try to monitor the bands each day and remember the WX conditions which are expected to produce the desired effect. Arranging a 'hot line' telephone network with other enthusiasts is a good idea, since the best reception can often last a very short period of time and it may well be over by the time the SWL has finished mowing the lawn! A good policy is to monitor the 10 metres (28 MHz) band during low sunspot activity; if very strong European signals are being heard on that band there may occasionally be the chance that the VHF bands are also affected by ionospheric conditions. Disturbances to television reception may also be a guide to unusual conditions on the VHF bands and it is always worth checking. (Who wants to watch 'Crossroads' anyway?)

Conditions often vary from one part of the country to another. Stations in south-east England are particularly favoured because of their proximity to the Continent but they are by no means guaranteed the best conditions.

What has been written about the amateur bands is equally relevant to the broadcast band from 87 to 108 MHz. During good conditions continental BC stations may be heard and it is a useful policy to check for them.

Verifications

Just as people on holiday take photographs to prove to the neighbours that they *were* in Bangkok and not really in Blackpool, so too is the verification element of great significance in short wave radio. There are, however, important differences. Anyone who has been on holiday knows where he went and doesn't need to prove it to himself but a listener hearing an apparently rare station could have mistaken the identification or may even be hearing an imposter (or 'pirate' in radio jargon). How can one be sure?

In some instances it is quite apparent that an amateur station being heard is a fake but such stations are fortunately comparatively few. Radio amateurs are a shrewd bunch and can generally pick out the fraudsters and give them the cold shoulder. This is particularly so where the genuine amateurs have sophisticated antenna systems and can identify the direction from which signals are coming. Even without this assistance reception of some areas of the world is impossible at particular times of the day or on certain frequencies. The novice, though, will often not have the experience to identify the 'pirates' and will also have to contend with an even greater hazard.

Identification by stations is not always given clearly and there may be problems with interference from electrical or atmospheric sources or from other stations. Consequently, the newcomer to the hobby may be listening to a PY station in Brazil and think he is hearing a BY station in China, which would be a much more difficult catch. The listener cannot call the station to check the callsign and he could in good faith write the incorrect call in his log and add China to his list of countries heard. How can he avoid this pitfall?

Whilst listeners cannot *talk* to the stations they hear, they can generally communicate with them by correspondence, assuming that they have correctly copied the callsigns. A letter to the BY in the above example would not get very far (and would therefore cast some doubt on the reception), but a report to the PY could well produce a reply proving that the listener did indeed hear Brazil. It all sounds very simple but there is rather more to it than that. Reports sent to stations have to be meaningful and a communication which merely says, 'I heard you on 25 January at 1430 GMT. Please confirm that you were transmitting then', is a sure candidate for the waste paper basket.

Verification is equally relevant to broadcasting stations. Once again reports to the stations do have to be of value to them but different considerations apply. Amateur stations are mainly interested in talking to other amateur stations and reports from listeners are often superfluous, especially when they arrive long after the transmission to which they relate. Broadcast stations, on the other hand, exist so that an audience can listen to them and they are generally more likely to welcome reports; indeed, they often actively solicit them. Even so, those stations whose programmes are intended for reception only in their home countries are sometimes less than enthusiastic about reports from other countries.

It will be seen that getting replies to reports calls for some effort and occasionally ingenuity. The golden rule in all cases is to provide stations with as much helpful information as possible. Some stations will answer scrappy reports but the vast majority will not. In all honesty they should not have to make the choice; the hobby of short wave listening is demeaned by those few listeners who do not take the time to compile proper reports but nevertheless expect replies.

Since reporting to amateur stations is somewhat different from reporting to the broadcasters, it is necessary to deal with both aspects separately; we will start with the amateurs.

All SWLs should keep a logbook of the stations (or at least the most interesting stations) that they hear, even if they do not intend to send out reports. Unlike radio amateurs, who are invariably compelled to keep a log as a condition of their licences, listeners are not subject to the same discipline, but the sense of keeping a log does not need much explanation and it would be unusual to find a keen listener who did not have such a record. If one is to send out reports, the use of a logbook is imperative.

Logbooks are available commercially but it is a simple matter to devise your own. A reasonably large notebook from a stationer's will often fit the bill, or a listener can use a loose-leaf system (A4 size recommended) and keep the sheets in a binder. This latter method is

Right *Amateur bands logbook.*

the one I prefer, though if the sheets are duplicated or photocopied it may well be more expensive than having the standard type of logbook.

The type of layout which I use is shown in the illustration of a page from a typical logbook. It will be seen that not all of the items have been completed since some did not apply and other information was not obtained during the contacts.

Each entry shows the date and the time in GMT, Greenwich Mean Time being almost always used in short wave radio. This is also known as UTC, Universal Time Coordinated. British Summer Time (BST) is one hour ahead of GMT/UTC. The station heard is shown in the third column and the signal report of the station in column 4. 'QSB to' indicates that there is fading on the signal; this can affect both the readability and strength of the signal and the lower reports resulting from the fading are shown in that column. The standard meanings of the Readability, Signal Strength and Tone codes were given on page 47.

Column 6 indicates whether the station heard was working (talking to) another station (W), calling another station or calling CQ (C). Since both stations in a QSO may be audible, columns 7 to 9 allow details of the second station to be shown on the same line. Where the intention is to send out reports to one or both of the stations heard it is important that the calls are copied correctly since an amateur will check the details in his own log and if the listener has made a mistake with the callsign of one of the stations the entries will not tally.

As we have already seen, clarity of reception of stations may be affected by electrical interference (QRM) or atmospheric interference (QRN). The extent of the interference is shown in columns 10 and 11 by three crosses: X signifies light interference, XX shows fairly heavy interference and XXX indicates strong interference under both QRM and QRN headings. N indicates no interference at all. Where the source of the interference is known (*eg* adjacent stations, deliberate jamming, fluorescent lights, television timebase, *etc*) this can be shown in an abbreviated form.

The next column takes care of the weather (WX) at the listener's location, and the next two columns show the name of the amateur operator and his QTH. This latter information will generally be given by the amateur and is worth noting if it is heard.

DATE (1)	GMT (2)	STN HEARD (3)	RST (4)	QSB to (5)	C/W (6)	STN C/W (7)	RST (8)	QSB to (9)	QRM (10)	QRN (11)	WX (12)	NAME (13)	QTH (14)	QRG (15)	LANG (16)	REMARKS (17)	QSL OUT (18)	QSL IN (19)
3/8/86	1153	EA5DNO	57		W	G4XCX	58		N	N	RAIN	RAY	CASTELLON	28.550	E			
	1718	UZ3DXW	58		W	OK1DAU	47		N	N	RAIN	ANDY	MOSCOW	14.185	E			
	1722	UC2IJ	58		W	PA0DOH			X	N	RAIN	NICK	GRODNO	14.151	E		10/8/86	30/11/86
	1728	IK0GBM	57	56	W	G3SED			N	N	RAIN			28.525	E			
	2130	BP6OM	57		W	EC1COK			X	N	OVER CAST	JEAN		21.188	E			
	2132	PPSZAA	54		W	G4WEU	55		N	N	OVER CAST	GEORGE		21.242	E			
	2138	LU7EMZ	58		W	OH1ZA			X	N	OVER CAST	CLAUDE		14.183	E			
	2143	YV5PV	47		W	G4HJB			X	N	OVER CAST			14.168	E			
	2155	FG5BM	59		W	F6BBH	47	Q4 57	N	N	OVER CAST			14.108	F		10/8/86	
	2204	PT7AUT	47		W	SP5DRH	47		X	X	OVER CAST			7.080	E			
4/8/86	0845	OK2YUU	589		W	OH2BJR	579		N	N	FINE			14.072	E			
	0649	SP4VAG	589		W	VA1AZZ			X	N	FINE			14.068	R			
	2312	YO3VU	47		C	CQDX			TVI XX	X	RAIN			3.796	E			
	2320	N4MJH/SB4	58		W	VE1YX	59		X	N	RAIN	AMIR	NICOSIA	7.083	E	VE1YX WAS BOB BRIDGWATER		
	2325	ZD8SW	45	54	W	I8ZJK	58		X	X	RAIN			7.045	E			
6/8/86	2330	YC2GHE	46	55	W	UC1AWC	57		X	N	FINE			7.075	E			

The frequency (QRG) of the transmission is shown in column 15 in Megahertz. Many older receivers and some general coverage sets do not have the facility for reading frequency to the nearest kilohertz and in these cases one can only show the reading to the nearest tenth or hundredth of a Megahertz.

When the SWL is able to log stations in languages other than his own, it is useful to show in column 16 the actual language being used (E = English, F = French, *etc*). This is not purely for egotistical reasons since if a station does not understand English and one can subsequently write to him in his own language, it improves one's chances of getting a reply; it is worth being reminded of this when making out reports.

The 'Remarks' column can be used for any other relevant information, such as whether a station was the first one heard from a particular country, brief details of the conversation heard which can be used in a report, *etc*. Any changes in equipment used should be shown and if one has a choice of receivers and antennas it is important to show which one was in use at the time. The name and QTH of the station being worked can also be shown. Where contacts are of a quick-fire nature, as during contests, it is useful to list a number of stations contacted so that this information can be given if a report is sent to the station. It is better evidence of reception than a mention of only one station. The final columns show the date when a report was sent to the station (QSL out) and the date a reply was received (QSL in). Unfortunately the latter column is used less often than the former!

In the course of a listening session many stations will usually be heard and one would need a large number of logbooks to record them all. Moreover, it will be difficult to locate specific entries if the logs are too voluminous. For this reason, most experienced listeners prefer to record only the most interesting stations. For the novice, however, this policy can have serious drawbacks, as we will see later.

As a minimum, it is suggested that each year the logbook should show at least one station from each country heard on each band. This provides useful background information and allows one year to be compared with another. However, it is obviously far better to be more comprehensive as that will permit seasonal variations to be studied and highlight the times of day when good reception is most likely.

For those with suitable computer equipment, a logbook can be compiled by this means and that can have very positive advantages when one wants to send out reports.

Most reports to amateur stations from listeners are sent by way of QSL cards (or, to be more accurate, SWL cards). These show the listener's name and address and his club membership number if he belongs to a club. They are completed with information from the listener's logbook. Some cards are available commercially with a standard layout which can be adapted to a listener's own requirements. The important thing to ensure is that the cards contain enough information to be of use to the recipients; it has to be admitted that some of the cards available as standard designs from printers do not always comply in this respect. They can nevertheless be used providing that additional information is written on them before despatch, but it is preferable to obtain a better card at the outset. Designing one's own can be fun and a card with an individual appearance may attract more attention than a standard design.

Amateurs generally receive QSL cards automatically from stations whom they work as a verification of their contacts and it is unfortunately the case that very few reports from listeners can tell them anything they do not already know. At the same time, printing and postage costs do not come cheap and the listener must inevitably start off at a disadvantage compared with the amateur who has spoken to the station being reported. The listener's report must therefore be as useful to the recipient as possible and we need to consider how we can achieve this.

The first thing to remember is that the amateur needs to be satisifed that the listener did in fact hear *him* and not somebody else. For this reason he must be told the date, time and frequency of the transmission. He also needs to know with whom he was in contact or which station he was calling. It is best to detail an actual contact if one results, and if some indication can be given of the topics discussed, so much the better; the signal report given to the other station may also be quoted.

When it comes to reporting CQ calls, great caution must be exercised. As in photography it is generally accepted that one should not point the camera into direct sunshine yet some startling results can very occasionally be achieved by ignoring this advice, so in amateur radio it is an established 'rule' never to report a CQ call since most amateurs completely disregard such reports. There are odd instances, however, when an amateur will welcome information about his CQ calls with open arms. This applies when no replies are received to the calls over a period of several minutes and the amateur gives up (in disgust, perhaps), probably thinking that his equipment is not functioning properly. If an SWL is able to send a report *quickly* to the station, preferably by airmail, and give as much information as possible (including details of any faults with the transmission such as poor speech quality or frequency drifting), it could be of considerable help to the station. However, such occurrences are few and far between and the unwritten rule about not reporting CQ calls will generally apply.

Secondly, the station being reported needs to know how well his signals were being received. This is where the Readability, Signal Strength and Tone indicators come in. A report should contain an *honest* appraisal of these factors. There is a tendency to exaggerate — and amateurs themselves are often guilty of this — but it must be avoided. If one misses half of what is being said because of interference the signal cannot be graded Q5 despite what one often hears on the air. Some people seem to think that the recipient of a report will be offended if he is given a Q3 S4 report and will not reply, but that is not borne out in my experience. In fact, the patronizing approach may have the opposite effect to that intended. If a European station is talking to an Australian and the latter is reported at Q5 S9, he may well think that he wasn't heard at all and that the listener actually heard the European!

The most useful reports are those which compare the signals of several stations in the same general area. If one is reporting to a station in Sydney, for instance, and can also show reports for other stations in Sydney or Melbourne or Canberra, this will enable the station to compare how well or how badly he was faring in relation to other eastern Australian stations. If no other Australians are being heard but stations elsewhere in Oceania are audible, a comparison should be made with their signals. However, if the station heard is the only one audible from that area over a period of, say, thirty minutes, it is a likely indication that he is doing rather well and he will want to know about it. The point should be made in the report.

Reports are likely to be of less value when the stations are nearer home, but the listener will understandably want to confirm every country that he hears. It is not difficult to hear European countries on the HF bands and reports to European stations should include comparative reports for other stations from the same country as a matter of course. At this stage of the hobby it is useful for the logbook to be utilized thoroughly to record all stations heard from a country which has yet to be verified, so that when a report is sent to, say, an Italian station he can be told how his signals compared with those of his fellow countrymen.

Many stations are heard only once but others are regularly active, sometimes at the same time every day. Quite obviously, few listeners can monitor the bands day and night, but when a station has been heard several times it is beneficial to record all the instances in the report with the usual details. Once again this is where the logbook comes in handy (and the computer handier still). In addition to the information already mentioned, the listener needs to show his name and address, his club membership number (if applicable) and details of his receiver and antenna.

A typical SWL card is depicted below, bearing a fictitious club membership number for the sake of the illustration. We will return to that in a moment.

QSL cards issued by amateurs are very similar in appearance, as will be seen from the photographs in this Handbook. They will of course show the type of transmitter and antenna in use but will not show details of other stations on the bands at the same time. The illustration overleaf shows the type of QSL card which might be received in reply to this SWL card.

Having written out his reports, what does the listener do with

SWL card.

100 ANYTOWN STREET, BIRMINGHAM B57 7RD
ENGLAND

_GL – 77777

To RADIO ..ZL4SSS...... Ur SSB/CW sigs hrd on 7. JAN.85...

at .0850. GMT on 14.173.. MHz clg/wkg .OH9KKK. RST..4.5..

QRM ...X... QRN ...X.... SSB to ...–..... WX ..Snow.....

Other stns in your area hrd today .ZL2XJY..0900. GMT. 4.6...

Remarks ..POOR CONDX. YOUR FT-301 WAS DOING WELL..........

RX: Trio JR-310. ANT: 66' long wire N/S at 25'.

Pse QSL direct or via Bureau.

73   JOE SMITH Joe

Z L 4 S S S

DAVID JONES, P.O. BOX 9988, DUNEDIN, NEW ZEALAND

To RADIO .*GL̶. 7̶7̶.7̶7̶7̶.*. This confirms my QSO on .*7. Jan 85.*...
at ...*0850*... GMT on ..*14.173.*. MHz. *CW*/SSB. Your sigs RST .
.........*—*....... Rig: FT301D - FL2100B. Power 400w.
ANT: 3 ele triband yagi at 20 metres.

Thanks for reports 73   *Dave.*

Amateur QSL card.

them? There are three possibilities: they can be sent direct to the
stations, to QSL Managers or to a QSL Bureau. Not all of the three
options are available in every case, so let us deal with them
individually.

For licensing purposes every amateur has to disclose his address to
the authorities. These addresses are printed in the *Radio Amateur
Callbook* which appears annually, in two sections: 'North American
Listings' and 'International Listings'. Although published in the
USA, these *Callbooks* are obtainable in Great Britain but are
expensive and tend to be bought only by people who use them
continually. Moreover, with addresses changing rapidly and new
amateurs becoming licensed, the information unavoidably becomes
out of date quickly. The 1979 *DX Listings* book (the former title of the
International Listings), for instance, contained 84,822 changes to
the previous edition! Some amateurs will give their addresses over
the air and this is obviously more reliable — and cheaper! Because of
the ever-increasing postage costs most amateurs and SWLs only use
the direct mailing method of sending QSL and SWL cards when they
badly need a reply or where there is no other means available.

DX stations in rare locations are now making increasing use of
third parties to handle their cards. That way they are able to free
themselves of the chore of sending out cards and can spend more
time making contacts on the air. The intermediaries, if one can call
them that, are known as QSL Managers and DX stations will
announce the callsigns of their Managers during QSOs so that

reports may be sent via them. The DX stations provide the Managers with their logbooks (or copies of them) periodically so that they can send QSLs to the amateurs who have worked the stations and reply to listeners who have sent reports. Some QSL Managers act for several stations — dozens in some instances. A similar thing happens when stations use special callsigns for various events and give their normal callsigns as a 'QSL Manager'.

For economic reasons the sending of cards direct to stations has declined over the years and most cards (even some which are intended to go to QSL Managers) now go via QSL Bureaux. These Bureaux are clearing houses for cards and are generally operated by the national radio societies of each country, though a few are run by other radio clubs and private concerns. Amateurs and listeners send batches of cards to their own Bureau and they are then distributed to other Bureaux world-wide. There are two major benefits to this: there is a very appreciable saving of postage, and one does not have to know the addresses of the stations. It sounds too good to be true? Well, yes and no. The big drawback, of course, is that it all takes far longer than sending reports to the stations or their Managers direct. It is not unknown, in extreme cases, for five years to elapse between a report being sent out and a reply being received. The ratio of replies to reports is also lower than with direct communications. But if one wants to send out a lot of reports — and some listeners despatch hundreds every year — the use of a QSL Bureau is very strongly recommended.

Before describing the operation of a typical QSL Bureau it needs to be stressed that the two-way use of a Bureau is confined to members of the organization which runs it. The Bureau operating in Britain is under the auspices of the Radio Society of Great Britain. The Society issues membership numbers and these need to be shown on SWL cards for identification purposes. The financial arrangements for the Bureaux vary from organization to organization: sometimes the service is fully included in the cost of club membershp, other societies may ask for a separate subscription to the QSL Bureau from those who want to use it, and it is quite common for clubs to ask members to provide their own stamped addressed envelopes for replies.

Let us now return to GL-77777, whose SWL card we were studying a little while ago, and assume that his number was issued by a club which has a QSL Bureau. He wants to send his card for ZL4SSS (a callsign also manufactured for the purposes of the example, though such a call, if actually issued, would indicate a New Zealand station) to his QSL Bureau, together with two or three dozen other cards for different stations throughout the world. What is the sequence of events?

Firstly, he bundles up the cards and sends them in one envelope to his British Bureau, paying only the UK postage on the envelope. When they arrive, the cards are sorted into countries and associated with other cards for those countries held at the Bureau. The ZL4SSS card joins the others for New Zealand, and when there are sufficient to justify the postage costs the British Bureau sends them to the New Zealand Bureau. When the latter has sufficient cards to send to ZL4SSS it will despatch them to him. If ZL4SSS decides to reply to GL-77777 he sends his QSL to the New Zealand Bureau and the procedure operates in reverse, with the British listener eventually getting the card with others from the British Bureau.

Since it is standard practice to maximize the benefits of posting in bulk, it follows that stations who are relatively inactive get infrequent deliveries of cards via the QSL Bureaux network and the time taken to get replies is increased accordingly. Likewise, where there are few stations licensed in a country it may be a long while before a distant Bureau will have enough cards to justify the expense of mailing them. Another problem arises where the intended recipient of cards is not a member of the organization which runs its national Bureau, and the cards may not be forwarded to him. Some years ago a European country had two radio clubs each with its own bureau and they seemed to be at loggerheads with each other, with the result that cards were not sent from one to the other for the benefit of the other's members. Some countries with few radio amateurs do not have radio societies and there is often little point in sending cards for those stations to the local Bureau since they cannot be delivered. (However, some of the more efficient Bureaux will identify the calls involved and send the reports direct to the stations concerned or to known QSL Managers, though that is not really the proper function of a Bureau.)

With cards going through so many hands it is clear that the use of a bureau is much slower than direct mailing. An additional delay is caused in some countries which have a great many amateurs because the HQ of the Bureau appoints sub-managers to distribute cards to groups of members and that is yet another link in the chain. Many people who use a bureau for the first time express great dissatisfaction with the service when they do not get any replies within the first few months. This attitude displays a basic misunderstanding of the way the system works and is not justified. Replies generally take a minimum of six months from despatch of report to receipt of reply and anything less than that is unusual, except perhaps for reports to stations in one's own country. The average time for a reply is one to two years.

The question of return postage is one that often confuses newcomers. Generally speaking, if a listener asks for a reply direct to his home address he should enclose return postage in the form of one or more International Reply Coupons, obtainable at main Post Offices. One coupon will normally enable the amateur to prepay a letter by surface/sea mail to an overseas country, whereas two or three coupons are needed for airmail transit. Countries which are not members of the International Postal Union do not issue or accept IRCs and they will be of no use to the stations in those countries for postal purposes, though they do have other uses: some people use them to buy subscriptions to overseas clubs or magazines. Russian stations are required to send their cards to the Russian QSL Bureau — the highly efficient Box 88 in Moscow — and are not supposed to mail cards direct, so it is a waste of money to send IRCs to them. Several South American countries do not recognize the coupons because they belong to a different Postal Union which, it is thought, issues its own coupons. Where the listener is happy to receive a reply via the QSL Bureau it is not necessary to send return postage.

The old maxim that 'you get out of it only what you put in' has some relevance to QSLing and, as already explained, good reports are likely to be more successful than mediocre or downright bad ones. Even so, the ratio of reports to replies is hardly ever satisfactory. Many listeners get replies from only about one in five reports and a 40% report/reply ratio is very good for reports sent in quantity through a QSL Bureau. Those listeners who QSL selectively for good catches and send their reports direct to the stations or their Managers with return postage will do much better and may even achieve a return of as high as 75%. If one particularly needs a card for a new country verified or for a listening award it is worth making this point on the card as it often has the desired effect when the report has obviously been compiled with care.

Unlike amateur stations, broadcast stations operate to fixed and published schedules and reports to them need to be compiled differently. I have never seen any commercially produced logbooks for BC stations and amateur logbooks are unsuitable. The listener should therefore draw up his own.

BC stations do not use the Readability, Strength and Tone codes used in amateur radio but have their own SINPO code. The letters which make up SINPO stand for Signal strength, Interference, Noise, Propagation and Overall merit, and each item is rated on a scale from 1 to 5. A station with excellent signal strength, suffering no interference (QRM) and no noise (QRN), with no propagation disturbance (QSB) and therefore of excellent listening quality would rate as 55555. The actual graduations in the codings are as follows:

S (Signal strength)	I (Interference)	N (Noise)
5 Excellent	5 Nil	5 Nil
4 Good	4 Slight	4 Slight
3 Fair	3 Moderate	3 Moderate
2 Poor	2 Severe	2 Severe
1 Barely audible	1 Extreme	1 Extreme

P (Propagation disturbance)	O (Overall merit)
5 Nil	5 Excellent
4 Slight	4 Good
3 Moderate	3 Fair
2 Severe	2 Poor
1 Extreme	1 Unusable

Logbooks of BC stations should show the date and time in GMT/UTC and the frequency on which the station was transmitting. Frequencies are often announced during the programmes for the benefit of listeners whose receivers are not capable of determining the QRG with sufficient accuracy. Many stations transmit on more than one QRG simultaneously and it is a good idea to check all the channels so that comparative reports can be sent to the stations. Each frequency should be shown in the log with a SINPO report. Where stations are transmitting on more than one channel in the same band care must of course be exercised to ensure that the right frequency is shown in the log.

Since BC stations will expect to be given details of the programmes which the listener heard, it is desirable to listen to a station for a minimum of fifteen minutes and to record in the log full details of what was heard. Titles of programmes can often be obtained from station programme bulletins and do not really prove that the station was heard. What is really required is something along the lines of the following:

2000 Opening of transmission; news in English by male news-reader.

2005 Comments on the news, including opinion on exploration for mineral deposits.

2010 Letters from listeners in Africa.

2015 Western 'pop' songs, including 'The Power of Love' by Frankie Goes to Hollywood.

2023 Interviews with visiting football team players.

2028 Closing news headlines.

2030 End of transmission in English; opening of service in French.

BC stations like to feel that listeners are really interested in their programmes, not merely trying to cadge QSL cards, and they always welcome comments about their shows. These could be shown briefly in the log.

Of course, listeners cannot enjoy the programmes if there is so much QRM or propagation disturbance that they cannot hear them properly. Stations rely on their audiences to draw their attention to particular problems. If reception is difficult because of a stronger station on a nearby channel they want to know about this so that they can consider moving to a different frequency when their next schedules are being planned. Consequently, the source of QRM should be noted and the station advised, since this may be the most interesting part of your report when you write.

Because of the regular broadcasting patterns of BC stations one can often compile a report based on several transmissions and this should be done wherever possible. When the SWL has enough information to write to the station he needs to give his name, address and club membership number (if appropriate), details of his equipment, full details of the times and frequencies of transmissions with SINPO reports and summaries of the items heard in the programmes. If other stations were being heard from the same area, details of these transmissions should be shown together with SINPO reports. There is no need to give details of the programmes being broadcast by these other stations.

Listeners will occasionally hear requests for reports to be made using the SIO code. This is, in effect, the SINPO code without the 'N' and the 'P'. If that is what is required it is undoubtedly advisable to comply, but it is best to use the SINPO code at all other times.

Although it is not unknown for QSL Bureaux to handle reports for BC stations it is nevertheless rare and it is now almost universal practice for listeners to send these reports to the stations direct. Where reports are solicited, as is often the case with international broadcasters, the mailing addresses will be given over the air. Other addresses can be obtained from the *World Radio TV Handbook* if not given in Appendix 8.

Many of the most interesting catches on the broadcast bands will be stations transmitting in the language of their own country and not aiming for reception in far-off countries. In these instances reports in English may not be understood and could therefore be ignored. If possible, therefore, listeners should make an attempt to send a report in the language of the country concerned. These stations may also be unfamiliar with the SINPO code and a brief summary of the quality of reception could usefully be included. Even when the SWL has gone to the trouble of compiling a letter in a foreign language there is still no guarantee of success since it is sadly the case that some stations are totally uninterested in reports from outside their normal catchment area. South and Central American stations and West Africans have a particularly poor reputation in this respect.

Whilst the larger stations will often reply without return postage, most of the smaller ones are likely to be more responsive if an IRC is enclosed and there is much to be said for erring on the side of generosity. This is especially so if one is requesting not only a QSL card but also programme schedules which can be expensive to mail. Some stations are inclined to send other items as well, such as pennants, report forms for future reports, *etc*, and some have been known to send piles of literature containing propaganda for the political system of the country. During the Chinese Cultural Revolution there was a joke going around that postmen whose rounds were populated by short wave listeners spent more time on sick leave suffering from backache than actually delivering the mail!

QSL cards of the type used by amateurs are not suitable for reports to broadcasting stations but the stations themselves will often reply with their own QSL cards. The smaller stations, though, will not have QSL cards and may not even know what they are. It is a good policy to ask these stations to verify reception with their QSL card *or* a letter. Provided that the letter contains enough information to prove reception it can be counted as a legitimate QSL and will be accepted as such by organizations issuing awards. The report/reply ratio for broadcast stations depends to a large extent on whether one is reporting to the large or small stations and one's ability to report in foreign languages. It is easy to obtain verifications from the international broadcasters but a different thing entirely when trying to confirm the rarer stations. Perhaps that is what makes the whole thing such a challenge.

Measuring Achievements

'Have you ever heard Australia?' Tell people that you are a short wave radio listener and that is a question they are almost certain to ask. It is surprising how many people, who might be expected to know of the existence of New Zealand if not of the other Pacific islands, think that Australia is the furthest point geographically from Britain and therefore to hear a station from there must represent the pinnacle of achievement. In reality, it is fairly easy to hear Australia on both the amateur and the broadcast bands but, to be fair, it is not unreasonable for those unfamiliar with short wave radio to think otherwise.

Short wave radio is often highly competitive, with listeners taking part in contests and merit tables in magazines and applying for awards, but the point needs to be made at the outset that no-one is under any pressure to get involved in competitions of any sort. The BC bands fan who is perfectly content to listen only to his favourite stations will not be derided by others whose sole interest is in chasing DX. Likewise, the amateur bands SWL who listens only to his local amateurs will not be ridiculed by the DXer who has 300 countries to his name. One of the great features of short wave radio is that it allows all listeners 'to do their own thing'. There is no doubt, though, that DXing can be very exciting and that many listeners do enjoy the challenges that it affords.

With the vast number of short wave radio stations licensed, it is obvious that no one person can hear every one. To do so is not even theoretically possible, since the possession of a licence does not necessarily mean that a station is 'active' any more than possession of a driving licence means that one owns or drives a car. Obtaining a transmitting licence calls for some effort and stations will not normally relinquish it unless they have decided quite positively that they do not intend to use it again. This applies to broadcasting stations as much as to amateurs. At the same time, many stations who are allowed to operate only on the VHF bands cannot possibly be heard at any great distance because of the properties of VHF propagation.

With far fewer stations licensed on the broadcast bands, listeners may well be able to say from their logbooks how many they have heard. This is certainly not the case on the amateur bands, though, since nobody records every single station heard, except perhaps during the first few weeks of listening. Were they to do so they would need countless logbooks and probably a bigger house in which to store them! The 'numbers game' does have a relevance to contests, as we shall see in the next chapter, but not to everyday listening.

When it comes to measuring achievement on the short wavebands we do not look at the number of stations heard but at the number of countries, zones and possibly prefixes for amateur stations. The ultimate achievement would be to hear every single country on every band but nobody has yet done this and it is unlikely that anyone ever will! The reason is that some countries are not allowed to use all of the bands — and a few countries cannot at present use *any* of them. Nevertheless, all of the countries of the world have seen some activity on the amateur bands during the past twenty or thirty years and a very select band of SWLs who have been active for many years have succeeded in getting every country but only by utilizing all the available frequencies.

The obvious question which now arises is: what constitutes a country? One could write reams on this topic, which is an endless source of controversy. Readers who study Appendix 2 will be in for some surprises. No-one doubts that Belgium, Bolivia and Algeria are countries, but what are we to make of St Peter & St Paul Rocks, United Nations New York and Desecheo Island? Who decides what is a 'country' anyway?

Any radio club can compile its own Countries List for the use of its members and also for anyone else claiming its awards. Most societies, however, are strongly influenced by the Countries List published by the American Radio Relay League (ARRL), which is often known as the DXCC List for reasons which will be mentioned later. The ARRL, which is the national organization for radio amateurs in the USA, has a Committee which decides which countries to accept and also publishes general guidelines, though it does not always appear to stick to them. In addition to recognizing countries which are internationally accepted as such, it also takes into account the administration of other locations and, in the case of overseas possessions, their distance from the mainland. For instance, although Alaska and Hawaii are States of the USA they are recognized as 'countries' in their own right because of their distance from the other forty-eight States. Likewise the Galapagos Islands, although under the jurisdiction of Ecuador, are recognized as a separate country for reasons of distance. In the case of Brazil, the islands of Fernando de Noronha, Trindade and St Peter & St Paul Rocks are all considered as 'countries' separate from the mainland. Some islands do not appear to be owned by anyone (!) or have disputed ownership, such as Spratly Archipelago, and these are recognized separately. Sovereign bases on the territory of another country, such as the NATO bases in Cyprus, count apart from the host country. Even buildings sometimes get into the act: the United Nations premises in Geneva and New York are regarded as different 'countries' from Switzerland and the USA, however ludicrous that might appear to casual (and some not-so-casual) observers.

Political considerations also enter into the reckoning. Although it is necessary for South Africans and nationals of other countries to produce valid passports before being allowed entry to the 'homelands' of Transkei and Bophuthatswana, and the ITU has allocated those places block callsigns, the ARRL regards those locations as part of South Africa and does not accord them separate status. They also regard Walvis Bay as a part of South West Africa/Namibia, although it is actually a part of South Africa and ought to qualify as a separate country for the same reason that Alaska is so recognized. There is also an interesting case for regarding Antarctica as more than the one country allowed, since different parts of that huge continent are administered by different countries.

It is at this stage pertinent to enquire how some of these oddball 'countries' came to be accorded country status in the first place. To provide additional interest for those amateurs who had achieved almost all of what there was to achieve, in the mid-sixties conscious efforts were made to create more 'countries', and these generally came about as a result of DXpeditions in which a group of amateurs chartered a boat and set sail on the high seas. They called at islands previously known only to the compilers of navigational maps and subsequently claimed 'country status' for them. Several were recognized in their own right whilst others were grouped together as a single country when the distance between the islands was not great. These amateur 'boat people' provided a lot of interest around twenty years ago and most of the locations which they visited have subsequently been revisited by other amateurs. Of course, new locations have been visited too, but the ARRL has tended to examine applications for 'country status' more critically of late, and changes to the ARRL Countries List are now more often caused by political events affecting countries rather than additions of new places.

Any radio society may of course have its own Countries List, although in practice most bodies nowadays keep fairly rigidly to the ARRL List. The International Short Wave League, which unfortunately ceased operations in 1986*, used to recognize the subdivisions of Antarctica, the autonomous regions of Italy and the South African 'homelands', and it was not averse to including countries which had never been activated by radio amateurs if they satisfied its criteria for recognition.

It will be readily apparent from the foregoing that broadcast bands listeners are at a distinct disadvantage when it comes to collecting countries. All of the countries on the ARRL List have at some time or other been activated by amateur radio stations — some, admittedly, a long time ago — but no-one has yet established a broadcasting station on Desecheo Island and no-one intends to do so whilst the island is uninhabited! This ought at first sight to make things much easier for the BC bands enthusiasts who have far fewer places to hear, but in fact it is extremely difficult to log many of the distant locations where the stations use low powers. Hearing every available country on the BC bands is just as much an achievement as doing the same thing on the amateur bands.

It is important that broadcast bands listeners remember that stations count for the country where the transmitting station is actually located. This often involves some research, which can be very beneficial. For instance, Radio Nederland has relay stations at Bonaire and Madagascar and a listener hearing these stations is able to add Nederlands Antilles (Windward group) and Madagascar to his personal countries total instead of the Netherlands itself.

For listeners to the VHF bands, counting countries has its obvious limitations even when conditions are superb, and amateur radio SWLs often calculate their scores on the basis of the IARU QTH Locator of Europe, which divides the European continent and parts

*At the time of writing, efforts are being made to reactivate the League.

of Asia and North Africa into squares, denoted by two letters, for counting purposes. VHF operators almost invariably know the precise square in which they are located and will disclose this during QSOs. British amateurs, for example, might be in squares ZN or AM.

In addition to wanting to hear every country the DXer will also want to log as many countries as possible on each band and most people keep 'band scores' for this purpose. As we have already seen, some countries do not allow amateur activity on 160 metres and not every country has been activated on every one of the other bands. On the BC bands, stations can only transmit on the channels for which they have been licensed. The situation changes all the time and it would be a poor year if a listener did not hear at least one or two new countries on an individual band basis.

For the purpose of short wave radio the world is divided into zones and so we have another challenge facing us. In addition to logging countries on each band we can also log the zones as well. Since there are far fewer zones than countries this looks an easier achievement to attain, but it is not without one or two pitfalls. The first is that there is more than one Zones List...

Back in 1938 the original zoning system was devised by Radio Magazines Inc of New York. It divided the world into forty zones with titles such as Western Zone of Europe (zone 14) and New Zealand Zone (zone 32). Each zone contained from a part of one country to several countries. Zone 6, for instance, included only Mexico whereas zone 14 contained no less than twenty-five countries. Because of its sheer size, Asiatic Russia occupied the whole of two zones (zones 18 and 19) exclusively plus parts of other zones. As time has gone on, of course, there have been amendments to the countries in the zones but the actual zone boundaries have remained the same.

The zones referred to are widely known as 'CQ Zones' and are still used by *CQ Magazine* for its very popular contests. They are relatively easy to understand, the only minor problems arising with Canada, the USA and the USSR which, because of their size, are in more than one zone. The most difficult zones for the European amateur bands listener are zones 19 (Eastern Siberian Zone of Asia) and 23 (Central Zone of Asia).

Around a decade ago the International Telecommunications Union (ITU) devised its own zoning system and this has been accepted by national radio societies affiliated to the ITU. Whether it is an improvement on the 'CQ' system is questionable; I firmly believe that it is not and this opinion is seemingly shared by amateurs who refuse to have anything to do with it. The ITU system divided the world into no less than ninety zones and the problems of countries in more than one zone are thereby compounded. Asiatic USSR, which is to be found in four 'CQ' zones, gets into no less than thirteen 'ITU' zones, and several countries which are in only one 'CQ' zone, such as Chile, are placed in two zones in the most recent zone list. Moreover, it is not possible for a listener to claim all ninety zones, though he might hear them all without realizing it. This is because fourteen of the zones (numbers 76 to 89) consist only of sea, and only land-based stations are recognized when listeners are computing their scores. They may perhaps hear amateur stations operating from shipping and the operators may occasionally give their bearing in longitude and latitude — though they will never say which 'ITU' zone they are in because they are unlikely to know! An added peculiarity of the ITU list is that it is often referred to as 'the 75 zones' although, like the trombones, there are seventy-six which can actually be heard (numbers 1 to 75 and 90)!!

Magazines sometimes run tables to which readers are invited to contribute and they are generally based on countries and zones. Quite often they are based on countries heard all-time and those heard in the year in question. They may be broken down into countries and zones heard by band and, for amateur bands listeners, into morse transmissions and telephony. It is great fun competing in these tables and it always seems surprising that more people do not do so.

A development of recent years is competitions based on amateur radio prefixes. This came about at a time when new countries were becoming increasingly difficult to hear and provided an additional challenge for those people who had heard all of the countries on offer. The popularity of chasing prefixes has waned somewhat because of the enormous increase in the number of them (I gave up when I reached 2000!). Collecting prefixes is a fairly artificial matter anyway since the same station may use more than one callsign at different times although at the same location throughout. BC stations do not use prefixes in the amateur sense and BC bands listeners cannot therefore join in.

Some countries are divided into administrative areas and it is not unusual to find listeners 'collecting' British counties, German DOKs, USA States (or even American counties, of which there are several thousand) and Russian oblasts. This can be very challenging since one often has to rely on the station giving the required information over the air.

Most listeners like to prove that they have heard the stations shown in their logbooks and therefore set about collecting QSL cards for this purpose. Some are quite happy to have a single card from each country heard though others will try to obtain cards for each band on which a country has been heard. We ought perhaps to amend a statement made a little earlier to say that the ultimate achievement is not only to hear every single country on every band but also to *verify* reception of each one. That makes it even more difficult, of course, but here again there *are* SWLs who have verified reception of every country on the ARRL List on all bands combined, though very, very few of them.

It is a popular practice to adorn the walls of one's shack (radio room) with QSL cards. This is jokingly said to avoid the need for wallpaper, though many people use that as well! The cards always make a good talking point when visitors are present and they make a colourful picture even when they are not. It is not a particularly good idea to leave the cards *in situ* for a long time, though, for the writing on them tends to fade, especially if they are exposed to strong sunlght, and it is far better to change the display at regular intervals.

Before committing their cards to the shack walls, listeners may like to consider the awards which are offered for certain achievements. It is sometimes necessary for them to submit their QSLs when claiming these awards but in other instances a signed statement by club officials (if the awards are for the amateur bands) that the cards are held and have been inspected by them will be accepted by the body issuing the awards.

The most famous award of all is the 'DXCC' or DX Century Club. Issued by the ARRL and available only to amateurs (not SWLs), this award is for amateurs who have made two-way contact with one hundred countries. Naturally the ARRL Countries List is used to determine the countries, hence its alternative title of 'DXCC'. When the award was first issued many years ago it was an extremely difficult achievement for an amateur to work 100 countries, and possession of DXCC was regarded with some justification as a very fine effort. Nowadays, with over 300 countries on the List, the situation is very different but the award still retains its popularity.

Right *An award for the reception of amateur stations in fifty Commonwealth countries.*

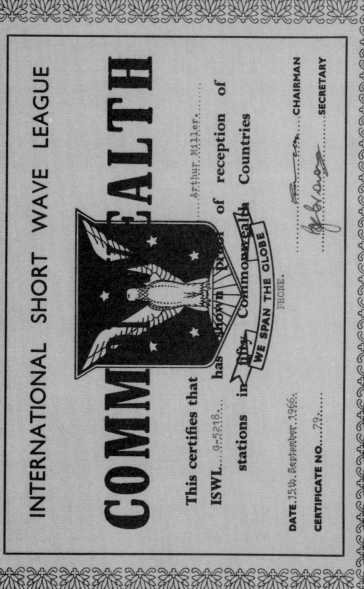

INTERNATIONAL SHORT WAVE LEAGUE

COMMONWEALTH

WE SPAN THE GLOBE

This certifies that

ISWL....G-5218.... has shown proof of reception of

stations in Other Commonwealth Countries

PHONE.

Arthur Miller........

DATE ..15th. September. 1966..

CERTIFICATE NO ....79......

........CHAIRMAN

........SECRETARY

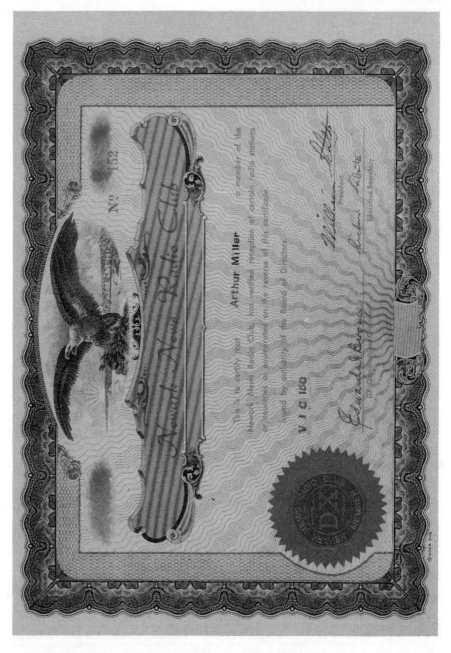

The Newark News Radio Club award is for verification of 150 countries.

It is no doubt a cliché, but there are 'awards' and 'awards' ... Some represent outstanding achievement and others don't seem to represent much more than that the recipient has parted with a sum of money to obtain them.

Many awards are issued by radio clubs and societies and may be available only to members or to all-comers. More often than not a charge is made to cover printing and postage costs and the issuing bodies often add on a contribution to their funds, though they will rarely admit it. The charges are sometimes waived completely when awards are issued to members. Almost all award-issuing bodies have their version of 'DXCC' using their own Countries List and generally provide stickers to add to the award for countries verified in excess of 100, often in steps of twenty-five countries. There are also awards for verifying all zones, verifying countries by continent, confirming prefixes, veryifying islands and so on. The actual qualifications needed give a good guide to the worth of an award. A certificate for confirming reception of ten zones would be fairly easy to acquire (but less so on the BC bands than the amateur bands), whereas one for verifying all forty 'CQ zones' would certainly be worth having and displaying prominently.

Not all awards involve reception of more than one country or group of countries. The popular 'Worked All Britain Awards' (WAB) divide the British Isles into over 4,000 areas (squares) based on National Grid reference and administration counties. Not all of the squares have resident amateur radio operators and they are activated only by portable or mobile stations who visit them for that very purpose. There are four main awards: WAB Overseas Introductory Award, WAB Areas Award, WAB Counties Award and WAB Large Squares Award. QSL cards are not required, logbook entries being sufficient, and there are special record books produced for the purpose. (Details from Brian Morris, G4KSQ, 22 Burdell Avenue, Sandhills Estate, Headington, Oxford OX3 8ED.) There is a similar type of award available for stations in West Germany. To obtain these awards it is usually necessary to spend a great deal of time on either the LF bands (especially 80 metres) or on VHF.

Amateur radio clubs sometimes issue awards to listeners (and of course amateurs) hearing/working their members. A certain number of stations have to be contacted and it is not unusual for the club's own transmitting station to provide bonus points. To celebrate some event of national importance radio clubs often issue awards to listeners who hear a small number of stations in their

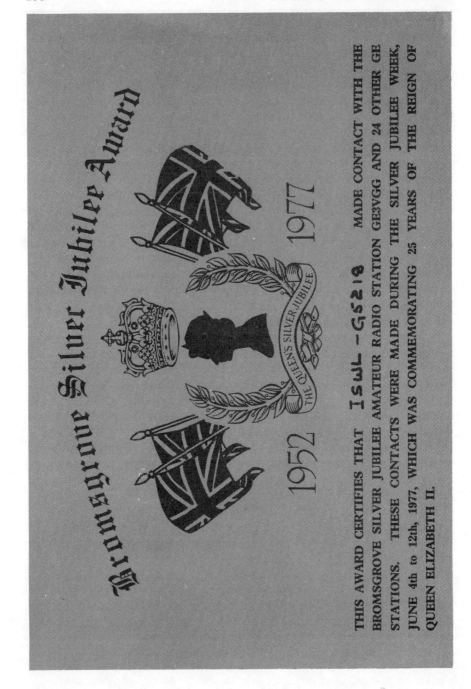

country during the period of festivities; details are usually announced over the air by participating stations or given in advance by radio club bulletins. There have also been odd occasions when listeners have received awards for which they did not apply and the existence of which they were unaware; this peculiar affair, which seems to make a mockery of the whole thing, has happened when the sole qualification for an award was the hearing of a particular station on a certain day or other period of time. Having sent away his reception report quite innocently, the listener has sometimes received not only a QSL card but also a certificate in reply!

It must not be taken for granted that all awards available to amateurs are automatically on offer to listeners as well. SWLs often come out second best in this respect. Before applying for an award — and certainly before sending off any QSL cards (which ought to go by registered mail abroad or recorded delivery in the UK) — SWLs must make sure by reading the award details that they are eligible to apply. Over the years more and more award-issuing bodies have come to accommodate listeners, which is heartening.

In Appendix 2 will be found an alphabetical list of countries generally recognized with their amateur radio prefixes, continents and 'CQ' and 'ITU' zones.

Left *An award for the reception of amateur stations in the Silver Jubilee Week.*

Contests

Sort wave radio contests and pop concerts have one thing in common; you either like them or you hate them. (They can also be very noisy, but we won't pursue that!) Some radio amateurs are scathing in their condemnation of them whilst others live only for the next one. They are not confined to the amateur bands though that is where they will usually be encountered.

For SWLs, contests fall into four categories. There are amateur radio contests for the amateurs themselves to which SWLs may listen and also contests specifically designed for listeners which may or may not be linked to transmitting contests. The latter are run by clubs and may be open only to their members or to anyone who cares to join in. Similarly, clubs organize contests on the broadcasting bands and broadcasting stations may have their own contests, the winners of which sometimes receive a free holiday in the country concerned. We can consider each type of contest separately.

Rarely does a weekend go by without a transmitting contest of some sort on the amateur bands. Some of these are major contests with participants throughout the world whilst others are of a more local nature often run by the national societies of individual countries and the existence of the latter may not be immediately obvious to casual listeners. In the major events, stations may have to contact other stations only in the country sponsoring the contest or any other station in the world; these latter ones attract tremendous support with the bands being packed with stations calling 'CQ Contest' or 'CQ Test'. Quite often individual operators or groups of operators visit rare countries to participate in these events and the benefit of this to SWLs is quite obvious. Hearing stations in more than one hundred countries in a contest weekend is commonplace, though not all of them may be taking part in the contest. What irritates some stations is that these contests virtually take over the amateur bands, making it difficult for effective non-contest QSOs. Stations who are not interested in competitive working not infrequently avoid being on the air when these events are scheduled.

Each transmitting contest has its own rules, but they need not concern us here. More importantly, from the angle of the listener, is that the major events always take place on the same weekends each year so that one can plan one's calendar around them. The most important and popular contests on the HF bands are shown below (all times are in GMT):

French REF-CW Contest	Last full weekend in January, 0600 Saturday to 1800 Sunday.
CQ-WW-160 metres CW Contest	Last full weekend in January, 2200 Friday to 1600 Sunday.
RSGB 7 MHz SSB Contest	First full weekend in February, 1200 Saturday to 0900 Sunday.
ARRL CW Contest	Third full weekend in February (48 hours).
CQ-WW-160 metres SSB Contest	Last full weekend in February, 2200 Friday to 1600 Sunday. ·
French REF-SSB Contest	Last full weekend in February, 0600 Saturday to 1800 Sunday.
RSGB 7 MHz CW Contest	Last full weekend in February, 1200 Saturday to 0900 Sunday.
ARRL SSB Contest	First full weekend in March (48 hours).
RSGB Commonwealth Contest (CW)	Second full weekend in March, 1200 Saturday to 1200 Sunday.
Bermuda Contest (CW/SSB)	Third full weekend in March (48 hours).
CQ-WPX-SSB Contest	Last full weekend in March (48 hours).
CQ-WPX-CW Contest	First full weekend in May (48 hours).
RSGB National Field Day (CW)	First weekend in June, 1600 Saturday to 1600 Sunday (may vary).

All Asia SSB Contest	Third full weekend in June (48 hours).
Venezuela SSB Contest	First full weekend in July (48 hours).
WAE-DX-CW Contest	Second full weekend in August (48 hours).
All Asia CW Contest	Last full weekend in August (48 hours).
WAE-DX-SSB Contest	Second full weekend in September (48 hours).
SAC-CW Contest	Third full weekend in September, 1500 Saturday to 1800 Sunday.
SAC-SSB Contest	Fourth full weekend in September, 1500 Saturday to 1800 Sunday.
VK-ZL SSB Contest	First full weekend in October, 1000 Saturday for 24 hours.
VK-ZL CW Contest	Second full weekend in October, 1000 Saturday for 24 hours.
RSGB 21/28 MHz SSB Contest	Second Sunday in October, 0700–1900.
RSGB 21 MHz CW Contest	Third Sunday in October, 0700–1900.
CQ-WW-SSB Contest	Last full weekend in October (48 hours).
CQ-WW-CW Contest	Last full weekend in November (48 hours).

It will be seen that most of these contests are organized by national radio societies such as the ARRL, RSGB and REF (France). The All Asia Contest is run by JARL (Japan), the WAE (Worked All Europe) Contest by DARC (West Germany) and the SAC (Scandinavian Activity Contest) by the Scandinavian society. Contests prefixed with the letters 'CQ' are organized by *CQ Magazine* and they are arguably the most popular of all since they allow contacts to be made with all other countries whereas most of the others restrict QSOs to certain countries or geographical areas. Where contests are shown above as lasting for 48 hours they always start at midnight GMT Friday/Saturday and finish at midnight GMT Sunday/Monday.

   To give some indication of what is possible for listeners during major transmitting contests, this chapter includes two graphs showing the number of countries I heard during the CQ WW SSB

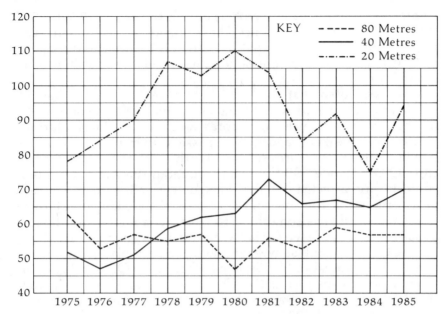

Above *Countries heard on 80, 40 and 20 metres during CQ-WW-SSB Contest, 1975–85.*
Below *Countries heard on 10 and 15 metres and All Bands during CQ-WW-SSB Contest, 1975–85.*

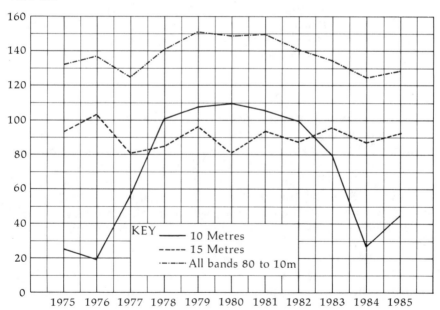

Contest (held annually in October) during the period 1975 to 1985. (They exclude 160 metres since I have only used this band in recent years. It must be stressed that listening on 160 metres during this contest is very rewarding — a good weekend will usually produce around forty countries.)

It will be noted that for five consecutive years more than 140 countries were heard on all bands combined in this contest. It is inconceivable that such high scores would be attainable during a non-contest weekend and it is impossible that any other contest would match these scores so consistently, such is the popularity of the CQ Worldwide SSB Contest throughout the world. Of course, contests are affected by the sunspot cycle like all other radio propagation, but the sheer number of stations taking part ensures that there is always something to hear. As a matter of interest, I usually manage to listen for between thirty-six and forty-two hours each CQ WW Contest weekend and tend to 'play it by ear' (an appropriate expression!) in deciding when to go QRT and get some sleep. If conditions favour the LF bands I will sleep in the daytime, but if 15 and 10 metres are wide open I will often have to wait until between 1800 and 2000 GMT on the Saturday night. Getting to sleep is no problem; getting up again afterwards is another matter and involves the use of at least two alarm clocks, one of which also makes the tea! Trying to listen for the full forty-eight hours is probably best not attempted since one's attention will wander at times of extreme tiredness and there is always the danger of falling asleep whilst actually tuning the RX. Inaccurate logging of callsigns is also likely.

Transmitting contests are fast and furious and listeners will need to have their wits about them. Newcomers may indeed find all the activity somewhat daunting. Most contest QSOs consist only of the exchange of callsign and a signal report together with the zone of the station (CQ or ITU zone depending on the contest), a serial number or the power being used. In the CQ Worldwide, G7AAA might give '5914' (*viz* QSA 5 S9 Zone 14), or in different contests '59150' (QSA 5 S9 Power 150w) or '59001' (QSA 5 S9 Serial number 001 — first station worked). Stations do not give their callsign for every QSO and it may be necessary to wait a little while before getting a positive identification. Although French and Spanish are widely used in the REF and South American contests (and of course Russian in the Russian events), the vast majority of contest operation takes place in English, which adds to the attraction of contests for many people.

Some clubs organize listening contests to coincide with the biggest transmitting events, but others like to steer clear of them. SWLs intending to participate in listening contests include those who set out with the intention of trying to win and others who merely want to join in the fun for a few hours. Contest organizers are always pleased to get logs from anyone eligible to take part and will welcome logs from people who have heard only a few stations just as much as those from the contest fanatics.

A contest which may be recommended to LF amateur bands listeners is the one run in January each year by the White Rose Amateur Radio Society. Covering 160, 80 and 40 metres and generally held on either the second or third weekend of the month, there are separate sections for CW and SSB and participants may log for a maximum of eighteen hours out of a twenty-four-hour period starting at 1200 GMT on the Saturday. This contest is open to all SWLs throughout the world, unlike most others (such as the RSGB HF Bands Contest) which are restricted to members of the organizing club. Details may be obtained from White Rose Amateur Radio Society, P.O. Box 73, Leeds LS1 5AR.

Serious competitors, if we may call them that, believe in doing some preparation in advance of the contest date (and this applies equally to broadcast bands listeners). They will not leave it to the last minute to study the rules, nor will they assume that the regulations are the same as they were when they last took part, since organizers sometimes vary the requirements. They will check the bands regularly as the contest date approaches to get an idea of which bands and listening times are likely to be the most profitable. They will study the scoring system in detail, for each station heard will not necessarily carry the same number of points and they could end up with a massive log which will still not give them much chance of winning.

Some organizers restrict the number of stations which may be claimed from each country, in which case the SWL needs to keep a running total to make sure that he does not waste time logging stations which are ineligible for points. Others do not allow more than a certain number of stations talking to the same amateur. Another variation is where only a limited number of hours can be spent logging, say eighteen hours out of twenty-four. More often than not, only stations who are actually in contact with other stations may be claimed and the callsigns of both stations have to be shown. This, of course, excludes stations making CQ calls or those who call stations which do not reply. It is important not to get so carried away in the excitement that callsigns are not properly identified, since logs containing obvious errors may well be rejected and the listeners disqualified. At the same time the logs must be written legibly if they are to be accepted.

Scoring in listening contests on the amateur bands usually entails logging as many stations as possible in as many countries as possible during the contest period. More points are sometimes awarded for stations outside one's own continent. The number of countries heard is then multiplied by the number of points for stations heard. This may be done on an all-bands basis or an individual band basis. Let us assume that each station counts one point and that the SWL in an LF bands contest hears ten stations in two countries on 160 metres, fifty stations in fifteen countries on 80 metres and twenty stations in ten countries on 40 metres. Using the all-bands method of scoring he multiplies $(10 + 50 + 20 =)$ 80 stations by $(2 + 15 + 10 =)$ 27 countries to give him a score of 2,160 points. On an individual band basis he scores $(10 \times 2) + (50 \times 15) + (20 \times 10)$, or 970 points. There are, however, numerous permutations and mastering the scoring system before the contest actually begins will often be of benefit in determining the contestant's approach to the contest.

In addition to HF contests on the amateur bands there are also regular contests on the amateur VHF bands. These tend to be of fairly short duration, say four hours or so, and are normally organized by national radio societies for their members, including listeners. Scoring is based on the distances of the stations from the listener's QTH. Occasionally a good spell of sporadic-E or tropospheric conditions will produce reception of stations from outside the UK, but this is by no means assured.

When it comes to contests on the broadcast bands the need for advance preparation is even more significant. Because BC stations transmit to regular schedules it is possible to have a trial run before the contest takes place to get an idea of what stations are likely to be heard, on what frequencies and when. Naturally there is no guarantee that conditions will be similar during the contest proper, but at least one has an idea of what to listen for. Study of the *World Radio TV Handbook* and current radio magazines will also help. Cynics may claim that someone could actually 'win' the contest without even switching on the RX, but contest organizers are alert to this

Right *Contest certificate awarded in 1976.*

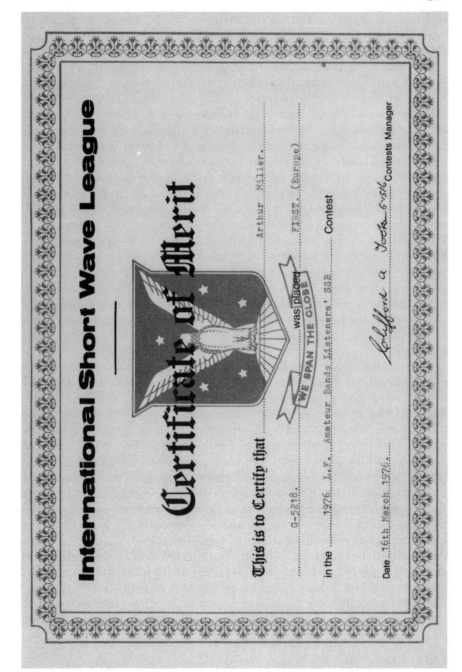

International Short Wave Wave League

Certificate of Merit

This is to Certify that .... Arthur Miller.

was placed .... FIRST. (Europe)

WE SPAN THE GLOBE

in the .... 1976. I.F. Amateur Bands Listeners' SSB .... Contest

Date ...16th March 1976......

.... Contests Manager

and usually insist on details of programmes being given in logs, or times of station identifications, so that cross-checking can be undertaken.

Having been a Contests Manager for the International Short Wave League for several years in the past, I have often been asked about the chances of bogus logs being submitted. Quite clearly, the whole credibility of contests relies on fraudulent logs being eliminated and it has to be admitted that someone does occasionally try to work a fiddle, though it is not a common occurrence. An experienced contests organizer — and such people are not chosen for their naïvety — can invariably pick out a blatantly false log within seconds of looking at it, and there are of course methods of checking logs which appear suspect without being obviously fictitious. If several entries in a log are found to be wrong there is little point in attempting to verify everything else and the whole entry is rejected. Contests managers will however take into consideration that the person involved may be a newcomer to the hobby who has been a victim of his own inexperience and will offer helpful advice in appropriate cases. But where there is evidence of deliberate fraud the perpetrator may well find himself not only eliminated from the contest but also thrown out of the club organizing the event if he is a member.

Something which tends to give the game away is that the persons submitting false logs invariably claim high scores. There is, after all, not much point in engaging in falsification if one does not get declared the winner. What satisfaction the 'twisters' get from being announced winners in these circumstances is a matter for the psychologists; certainly there are rarely financial benefits since most winners receive either certificates or cups. The extraordinary thing is that bogus entries are inclined to be so obvious. Two, particularly, come to mind. In the first case, the contestant reported hearing more than a dozen countries which had no legal amateur stations at the time (nor illegal ones, come to that!). The second instance was so ridiculous that even now it seems unbelievable. It happened in the days when there was a Sunday postal collection. The person was claiming to be logging hordes of stations on 10 metres right up until midnight on the Saturday night, which was four or five hours after the band actually closed. He then went on logging stations, or so he claimed, until the contest finished at 1800 on the Sunday, although

Right *Contest certificate awarded by the White Rose Amateur Radio Society.*

White Rose Amateur Radio Society

Know Ye All Men
by these presents that ~

ARTHUR MILLER

has achieved 2nd place S.S.B.

in 2nd S.W.L. L.F. Bands Contest.

and is hereby accorded this
Certificate together with all
titles and priveleges hereby.

By Command of the Committee
of the White Rose Amateur
Radio Society.

CHAIRMAN   SECRETARY

Dated this 1st day of June
in the year 1982

Serial No ~ 23.

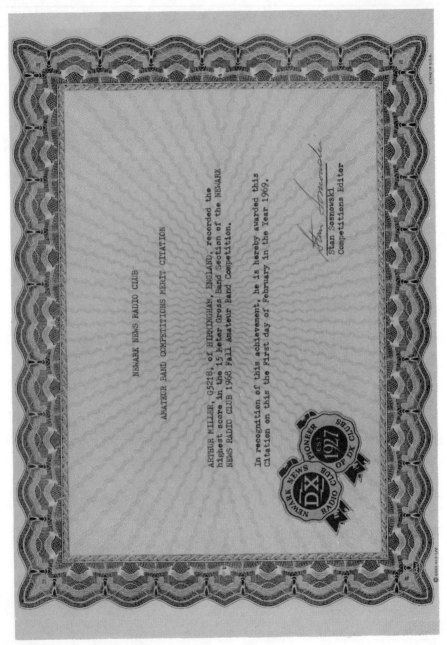

NEWARK NEWS RADIO CLUB

AMATEUR BAND COMPETITIONS MERIT CITATION

ARTHUR MILLER, G5218, of BIRMINGHAM, ENGLAND, recorded the
highest score in the 15 Meter Gross Band Section of the NEWARK
NEWS RADIO CLUB 1968 Fall Amateur Band Competition.

In recognition of this achievement, he is hereby awarded this
Citation on this the First day of February in the Year 1969.

Stan Sosnowski
Competitions Editor

Certificate awarded by the Newark News Radio Club in 1969.

his letter bore a postmark of 3 pm on the Sunday and was received by myself first post on the Monday! Had the contest been specifically designed for nitwits he would have justifiably won the first prize. As it was, he didn't win anything and made a fool of himself in the process.

It should not be assumed that anyone submitting a high score in a contest is automatically regarded with suspicion. On the contrary, all logs are considered genuine until found to be otherwise, in the best traditions of British justice! Those listeners who take part throughout a contest will naturally have much higher scores than those who listen for only a few hours. *Someone* has to win and by doing so will have recorded a higher score than the other competitors. Logs tend to cross-check with other logs but there is no certainty that any particular station will have been heard by more than one person. If an entrant lists a vast number of stations which are not in other logs there could be a valid reason for this, though it might initially look dubious. Some years ago the White Rose Amateur Radio Society of Leeds (mentioned earlier) ran its annual LF Amateur Bands Contest which happened to coincide with a Russian transmitting contest. This latter event provided dozens and dozens of stations for anyone with a minimal knowledge of Russian — and yet only two contestants even mentioned it when they sent in their contest entries.

Broadcasting stations which have their own competitions use them as a means of attracting more listeners to their stations. These events generally cover a period of several days and involve listeners answering questions about the country of the sponsoring station. The answers are normally to be heard in the course of programmes either transmitted during the contest period or before or after it. Sometimes the questions have a strong political bias, though that is not always so. The winners may receive an expenses-paid holiday in the country concerned as guests of the radio administration. It is sometimes claimed that these competitions are a propaganda exercise, though opinions differ. A friend who won one of these trips spoke very highly of it on his return to the UK.

The British Amateur Radio Transmitting Licence

Inevitably, the majority of short wave listeners who become hooked on amateur radio set their sights on becoming radio amateurs themselves. To achieve this objective is not quite as straightforward as people often seem to think, but that isn't necessarily a bad thing. Most listeners who are really serious about wanting to transmit can make the grade with appropriate study.

Before being allowed to transmit, a person must obtain a licence issued by the relevant authority and this invariably entails passing an examination to prove that one has the knowledge to operate a station efficiently and without inconvenience to other persons. With around two million radio amateurs throughout the world it is clearly important that the amateur bands should not play host to incompetent operators who would cause problems for everyone else. The licence requirements vary from country to country but generally the examinations consist of technical questions and a morse (CW) test, though some countries have more than one class of licence and not all of these require proof of the potential amateur's ability to receive and transmit morse.

The requirement for an amateur to understand and use the morse code is often queried. With telephony transmissions being so effective these days, what is the point of having to learn morse? The answer to this is that the amateur may be called upon to assist in providing radio communications during times of national emergency which could result in an absence of mains electricity, and in these circumstances a CW signal generated by portable equipment is more likely to be effective than a telephony one. (For instance, radio amateurs in England and Holland performed sterling service in most difficult conditions during the severe flooding of the Netherlands and the east coast of Britain in the 1950s.) It could also be argued that if the licence requirements were too easy there would be so many stations on the bands that operation would be virtually impossible most of the time!

For many years there was only one class of transmitting licence issued in Great Britain. To obtain such a licence one had to pass a technical examination (including questions on licensing conditions) and a morse code test, and only when the intending operator had satisfied the examiners of his abilities in both respects was a licence issued. For the first year after the issue of the licence the new amateur was allowed to operate only on CW and needed to keep a log to show that contacts on this mode had indeed been made. The technical examination involved writing answers to the questions posed and sometimes drawing circuitry or diagrams to illustrate the replies. Many people found these requirements too arduous and did not pursue their interest. At the same time, it is well known that some people become very nervous when tackling examinations and may not be successful even when they know their subject.

More recently there have been important changes with regard to amateur radio licences in Great Britain and these have generally made the acquisition of a licence much easier, though that is not to infer that the whole thing has become a push-over. There are three major changes:

1. In addition to the full licence, which allows operation on all authorized amateur bands, there is also a Class B licence which does not involve taking and passing a morse test. Amateurs with this type of licence cannot operate on bands below 50 MHz.
2. Full (Class A) licence holders are not restricted to CW during their first year of operation. They are not in fact compelled to transmit CW at all.
3. The technical examination is now conducted using the 'multiple choice' approach, in which candidates have to select the correct answers to the questions from three or four answers provided by the examiners. Whilst some purists feel this is a retrograde step it must be accepted that the examination is intended to test a candidate's knowledge of radio, not his ability to write intelligible English, and it is hardly likely that anyone who guesses most of the answers will succeed in passing.

Some enthusiasts commence as amateurs by passing the technical examination and obtaining Class B licences. At a later date they pass the morse test and then apply for Class A licences, which involves the issue of a new callsign in a different series. However, there is no time limit during which amateurs must pass a morse test and amateurs with Class B licences may retain them indefinitely without even attempting to upgrade.

The Department of Trade and Industry is responsible for licensing amateur stations in England, Scotland, Wales, Northern Ireland, Jersey, Guernsey and the Isle of Man. The Secretary of State for Trade and Industry has published an informative thirty-page booklet which gives full details of the licensing requirements in Great Britain and is essential reading for prospective radio amateurs. The booklet is entitled *How to become a radio amateur* and is available free of charge from the Secretary of State for Trade and Industry, Radio Regulatory Division, Waterloo Bridge House, Waterloo Road, London SE1 8UA. The remainder of this chapter is based on information contained in that publication and is published by permission of the Department of Trade and Industry, to whom I am indebted.

Before either a Class A or Class B license is issued, the prospective amateur must pass the Radio Amateur Examination conducted twice a year (usually in May and December) by the City and Guilds of London Institute, 46 Britannia Street, London WC1X 9RG. These examinations are generally held at schools and colleges where tuition has been provided but are not restricted to persons who have studied at those venues.

There are several schools and colleges throughout the country which provide tuition for both the Radio Amateur Examination (RAE) and the Morse Test. Particulars may be obtained from Local Education Authorities, the City and Guilds of London Institute and the Radio Society of Great Britain, Lambda House, Cranborne Road, Potters Bar, Herts, EN6 3JN.

The City and Guilds examination consists of two parts, which are taken on the same day with a short break in between. Part 1, which lasts one hour, is on licensing conditions and transmitter interference. Part 2, lasting ninety minutes, covers operating procedures, practices and theory. The actual composition of the papers is as follows:

Licensing conditions & transmitter interference

	Number of questions
1. Licensing conditions	20
2. Transmitter interference	15
	35

Operating procedures, practices and theory

1. Operating procedures and practices — 10
2. Electrical theory — 6
3. Solid state devices — 7
4. Receivers — 8
5. Transmitters — 8
6. Propagation and aerials — 8
7. Measurement — 8

55

For further information about the syllabus, readers should write to the City and Guilds at the address given earlier. A copy of the syllabus is available, as are sample questions, for a fee.

If a person passes one part of the examination but fails in the other he may retake the failed part at a later sitting without having to retake the entire examination.

Candidates sitting the RAE are issued with a record of their performance by the City and Guilds. Those who pass both components of the Examination (*viz* Parts 1 and 2) are issued with a certificate entitled The Radio Amateur Examination Certificate. This enables the person to apply to the Radio Amateur Licensing Unit, Post Office Headquarters, Chetwynd House, Chesterfield, Derbyshire S49 1PF, for a Class B amateur radio licence, if he so wishes.

Those who are not interested in a Class B licence and wish to obtain a Class A licence before commencing operating must also take a morse code test. The Radio Society of Great Britain (RSGB) took over responsibility for morse testing on April 1 1986 and has established a comprehensive network of test centres. Details can be obtained from the RSGB at the address shown earlier; envelopes should be marked 'Morse Tests (BR)'.

In the Morse Test candidates have to demonstrate their ability to receive and send the morse code to a high degree of accuracy at the rate of twelve words per minute:

(a) In the sending tests a candidate is required to send thirty-six words (averaging five letters per word) in plain language in three minutes without uncorrected error, not more than four corrections being permitted, and ten five-figure groups in one-and-a-half minutes without uncorrected error, not more than two corrections being permitted.

(b) In the receiving tests a candidate is required to receive thirty-six words (again averaging five letters per word) in plain language in three minutes and ten five-figure groups in one-and-a-half minutes. Each letter or figure incorrectly received counts as one error. A word in which more than one letter is incorrectly received counts as two errors. More than four errors in plain language and more than two errors in the figure test will result in failure. The tests do not include punctuation or other symbols.

Having passed the RAE and the Morse Test, the prospective amateur will be issued, without charge, with the Amateur Radio Certificate by the Post Office Radio Amateur Licensing Unit. This enables him to apply to the Licensing Unit at Chesterfield for a Class A amateur radio licence, provided he is over fourteen years of age.

Although fourteen years is the minimum age for a person to become a licensed radio amateur, the Amateur Radio Certificate is issued to anyone over the age of ten years who passes both the Radio Amateur Examination and the Morse Test. Persons in this category may operate the station of a licensed radio amateur under his supervision and using his callsign. With this exception (and another relating to national emergencies), persons who do not hold an amateur radio licence are not allowed to transmit on the amateur bands in any circumstances. It is not permissible, for instance, for members of a licensee's family to transmit unless they too hold licences.

A fee is payable for amateur radio licences. In 1986 this was £12 for both Class A and Class B licences. Licences are valid for one year, after which they may be renewed without any further tests or examinations. The renewal fee in 1986 was also £12.

Having obtained his licence the amateur must adhere strictly to the conditions under which it is issued, which are designed to protect other users of radio and electronic equipment as well as other amateurs themselves. The conditions are somewhat complex and the summary which now follows is necessarily abbreviated since readers who are particularly interested can read the full regulations in Appendix E of *How to become a radio amateur*. Anyone contravening the conditions runs a strong risk of having his operating permission withdrawn.

... The licensee can operate at his home address, at a temporary QTH subject to certain conditions, in a private vehicle or as a pedestrian. He may not operate from a vessel on the sea or within any estuary, dock or harbour, nor from an aircraft or a public transport vehicle.

... He may transmit messages of a personal nature in plain language, facsimile signals, radio teletype and visual images (amateur television).

... He may use the station during disaster relief operations or exercises related to the same conducted by the British Red Cross Society, the St John Ambulance Brigade, the County Emergency Planning Officer or any Police Force in the United Kingdom, and may exceptionally allow officials of those organizations to use his equipment.

... He may receive transmissions in the Standard Frequency Service, commonly known as Time Signal Stations. (As mentioned in an earlier chapter, SWLs are not authorized to receive these transmissions!)

... He must operate only on the specified amateur radio bands and must not exceed the transmitter powers allowed on those bands. Where bands are shared with other radio services, no interference must be caused to the other services. The licence conditions specify which bands and modes may be used and the power limits of each.

... Only personal operation by the licence holder or another licence holder (or young holder of the Amateur Radio Certificate operating under his supervision) is allowed.

... No general calls other than CQ calls made for the purpose of obtaining contacts are allowed.

... It is necessary for the frequency of a transmission to be stable and equipment must be available to verify the frequency on which the transmission is being made.

... No undue interference is to be caused to any other form of wireless telegraphy and tests have to be made periodically to ensure that this condition is being complied with.

... A log has to be kept of all contacts made and all CQ calls put out with details of operating times. These details have to be recorded in writing at the times of transmissions or immediately afterwards if it is unsafe to write them at the time, as in the case of an amateur operating from a moving vehicle.

... A receiver must be available for all bands and classes of transmission used by the amateur.

... Messages from other amateur stations may be recorded and played back to those stations but without the callsigns of the other stations being included in the replays. However, no gramophone or tape recordings of the type intended for entertainment purposes may be transmitted for any purpose.

... Callsigns are to be transmitted periodically for identification purposes. This is necessary when a station commences or ceases transmission or when there is a change of frequency. In long QSOs, callsigns are to be given no less frequently than every fifteen minutes.

... When a station operates from an address other than his licensed address this must be indicated. Stations operating from an alternative address give their callsign followed by '/A'. Portable stations use '/P' and mobile stations give '/M'. When a British station operates from another area of the UK with a different prefix, he must use the prefix relating to the country of operation. (G7AAA operating portable in Wales would use GW7AAA/P, for instance.)

... An amateur must make his station, licence and log available for inspection at all reasonable times by a person acting under the authority of the Secretary of State for Trade and Industry.

... The station must be closed down following a demand from the same authority.

... No business matters, advertizing or propaganda may be transmitted.

Although these regulations may at first sight seem highly restrictive they are nevertheless sensible and appropriate to a well-ordered operation of the amateur radio service.

Before concluding this chapter it is necessary to clarify one very important point. So as not to clutter the text with numerous references to 'he/she' or 'him/her', information has been presented using only the male version of the third person singular. However, amateur radio provides 'equal opportunities' for persons of both sexes and the regulations apply to women in exactly the same way that they apply to men. It is true that there are considerably more male amateur radio operators than there are ladies, but that is not the fault of the system. Amateur radio has much to offer the female members of the community, and more and more of them are coming to realize this. It is likely that as CB radio operators increasingly turn their attentions to the more versatile nature of amateur radio, the ratio of male to female operators will narrow — and only the most bigoted male chauvinists will take exception to that!

Citizens' Band Radio

The story goes that about thirty years ago two gentlemen were sitting at their listening post somewhere east of Harwich when they suddenly heard a host of unmistakably American voices talking about rubber ducks, smokies and choppers. At first they thought it was an escalation of 'the cold war', but they need not have worried. What they had really discovered was the start of Citizens' Band radio.

This tale is no doubt apocryphal, but it is tempting to imagine that it might well have happened. However, before we investigate further we ought perhaps to examine what Citizens' Band radio (or CB, as it is generally known) is all about. Because it is a form of communication involving individuals who are not professional broadcasters it is understandable that some people confuse it with amateur radio, but there are several important differences.

CB allows radio enthusiasts who may not have any technical knowledge of radio communication to contact other like-minded persons and discuss any topic of their choosing. Providing that they keep within the legal requirements of CB radio there is little restriction on their activities. They may talk to other stations from their homes or from vehicles and discuss current affairs, personal matters or traffic conditions. They may be marshals at fêtes, carnivals, pop concerts or sporting events. They may combine their efforts to assist in searches for missing persons or to help the authorities during national emergencies. Housebound people are provided with a link with the outside world and can summon help if needed. The range of possibilities is very large and is not confined to social activities. Businesses often equip their vehicles with CB radio so that their employees can be contacted when they are on the road in the vicinity of the firm's premises; taxi drivers and driving schools make good use of this form of radio. Lorry drivers are often CB radio fans who use CB to talk to other drivers or residents of the areas through which they are passing.

The main differences between CB and amateur radio can be listed as follows:

1. CB operators do not have to have any knowledge of the science of radio communication nor of the morse code and they do not have to pass any tests or examinations of competence.
2. CB enthusiasts are not restricted in the topics which they can discuss whereas amateurs must exclude politics, religion and business affairs.
3. The transmitting power authorized for CB stations is very low (rarely above ten watts), compared with one kilowatt maximum allowed to amateurs in several countries.
4. Excluding one VHF band which is rarely used, CB operators are confined to the 27 MHz (11 metres) band, which is suitable only for very local contacts for the greater part of each sunspot cycle. For this reason most QSOs are made with other CB stations in the immediate vicinity. However, during the years of greatest sunspot activity (about four years in eleven), DX contacts on the CB band can often be made and conversations between Europe and North America are relatively common.

Citizens' Band radio has until recently been regarded as an American activity. Around 1958 and 1959, during the peak of the sunspot cycle, many American CB stations were heard in Western Europe (and no doubt Eastern Europe too!) on 27 MHz. The hobby had not been long established at that time and there was a great deal of interest in it on the opposite side of the Atlantic. It was, however, difficult for European listeners to make much sense of it since the huge number of stations transmitting at any one time created a constant jabber and it was generally impossible to separate the stations on the RX so that their conversations could be rendered intelligible. Few European SWLs paid much attention to CB radio and as the propagation declined with the decreasing number of sunspots it was completely forgotten. The same type of situation prevailed during the next sunspot peak around 1970.

In the meantime the general public had made the acquaintance of CB radio via American TV programmes. Even then it did not register, despite the expression '10-4' ('over and out') becoming a national catchphrase after its use in the 'Highway Patrol' series.

It took an extraordinary combination of factors to launch CB radio in the UK in the mid-seventies. Had any one of these factors not been present the story might well have been different.

1. A recording artist, C. W. McCall, had a 'smash hit' in 1976 with a record entitled 'Convoy'. This told how a group of truckers (lorry drivers) used their CB radios to thwart the attentions of the law enforcement agencies on the highways. It was rather a banal tale delivered in a monotone but had the benefit of an extremely catchy chorus. Because the lyrics contained so much CB jargon the recording company provided written notes so that non-Americans could understand what it was all about. We learned, for instance, about 'smokies' and 'choppers'.

2. CB radio in Britain (and indeed in most European countries and elsewhere) was illegal. Many people seemingly enjoy breaking the law (as evidenced by under-age drinking, drug-taking and the like), and even those who would normally regard themselves as law-abiding citizens took a fancy to CB because they thought that the law was rather silly in this respect.

3. CB radio was strongly in decline in the United States and dealers were holding a lot of equipment which they could not shift.

4. The American economy was going through a very rough patch. The exchange rate had reached an incredible $2.40 to the £ sterling at the beginning of the decade. There was therefore a temptation for unscrupulous entrepreneurs to smuggle consignments of CB radio equipment into Britain because of the high profits to be made. At the same time, British nationals who had always wanted to visit the USA but had not previously been able to afford the cost took advantage of the exchange rate and the transatlantic air fares 'war' to have the holiday they had long wanted, and some of them risked bringing back their own CB radios afterwards.

5. We were approaching the peak of another sunspot cycle and reception of North American stations was very good. This gave the impression that CB operators could have DX contacts with other countries without the attendant formalities required by amateur radio.

Some European countries gave in to the pressure of the increasing CB activity and legalized the hobby fairly quickly. In Britain the authorities took a harder line, but as the number of unlicensed stations increased dramatically they set up a committee of enquiry to examine the subject. After rather a long wait the Government announced that CB was to be made legal in the UK with effect from November 1 1981, but that the mode of transmission was to be FM and the frequencies would be higher than those which most stations were then using.

Some pro-CB pressure groups were claiming prior to this announcement that there were two million people in Britain using CB equipment illegally. At first sight this figure seems fanciful but it may be more accurate than it appears. The Home Office admitted that it had received hundreds of thousands of complaints about illegal CB operations from people who had suffered interference to their TV reception or had had QRM on their radio sets, computers, record players, *etc*. Where several people in a block of flats or offices had complained, this was regarded as only a single complaint for the purposes of official statistics. It was clear that CB radio, as it was then, was creating enormous problems for many people. Naturally, some operators did have a knowledge of radio and were able to make suitable adjustments to their rigs to eliminate, or at least minimize, the problems, but most CB fans knew nothing of the technicalities of radio and probably didn't realize that they were being cursed by their neighbours.

There was no suggestion that anyone caused interference deliberately. On the contrary, most operators went out of their way to operate in a responsible manner because they realized that CB would never be legalized if the authorities were convinced that the hobby appealed mainly to crackpots. There was a very strong element of self-policing. Anyone using obscene or abusive language was quickly reprimanded by other fans. The real enthusiasts were convinced that CB had much to offer the community at large and did not welcome the idea of a few irresponsible operators jeopardizing their cause.

A strong social element grew up around the hobby. Fans organized themselves into clubs, which initially often had a large membership, and held regular meetings. They often ran well-publicized events and gave the financial proceeds to charity. Rarely can an illegal activity have been so openly conducted.

When the decision was reached to allow CB in the United Kingdom it was not welcomed unreservedly by its followers at that time. Scientific tests had shown that it was the use of the AM mode which was causing so much interference to other users of electrical equipment and AM therefore remained banned. FM was selected as the only legal mode and the frequencies allocated were forty channels in the upper portion of the 27 MHz band. Since most of the equipment available at that time used only AM on the lower portion of 27 MHz it was still legally unacceptable.

Manufacturers of radio equipment were not particularly accommodating. They went on record as saying that they thought the hobby was only a temporary craze which would last no more than three years. Few of them were prepared to produce the sets themselves though some said they might import CB goods. No-one showed any interest at all in the VHF band of 934 MHz, which was authorized in addition to 27 MHz. Comparisons were made with skateboards and, before them, hula-hoops.

When licences were first issued in Britain in November 1981 few of the claimed two million operators were waiting in the queues at Post Office counters. The maximum number of licences in issue at any one time was 350,000 in October 1982. Since one permit covered all members of a household the number of authorized users was obviously much higher than the total of licences in force but still far short of the alleged interest. Of course, it was likely that those people who intended to continue using their illegal equipment didn't wish to identify themselves by having their names and addresses on file.

CB radio is still with us but on a much reduced scale. The number of current licences has declined steadily; in May 1986 only 140,000 were in issue. Shops selling CB equipment have closed down and former fans regularly advertize their rigs for sale in the small ad section of newspapers. Many of the old AM transceivers have been consigned to the dustbin, though stalwart operators sometimes continue to defy the regulations by operating with that mode, and complaints of interference have not been completely eliminated. Possibilities of DX working disappeared with the sunspots and almost all contacts are presently of a purely local nature, though there are possibilities of contacts into Europe on sporadic-E or tropospherical propagation from time to time, especially in the summer months. CB clubs have not always survived but those that remain continue to provide a good service for their members and frequently hold the fund-raising events for charity for which they have established a fine reputation.

The most obvious question which now comes to mind is: what has happened to those CB operators who have abandoned the hobby? Many of them simply lost interest and moved on to other entertainments such as computers and video recorders. Their involvement in CB was only going to be transient anyway. Others took CB rather more seriously and used it as a means of studying radio communication and radio theory. Once they had realized the extreme limitations of CB they set their sights on becoming radio amateurs and spent their time obtaining the necessary qualific- ations. With an amateur radio licence they were afforded the opportunity of talking world-wide every day, not just when the sunspot cycle happened to be running in their favour.

Because so many keen CB enthusiasts have switched their interest to the amateur bands, the comment has been made that CB is a sort of 'kindergarten' amateur radio. This, however, is misleading. As we have seen, amateur radio and CB have many differences and some people are active on both. Possession of an amateur bands licence did not stop some amateurs from applying for CB permits too, if they wished to enjoy the free-and-easy operating allowed on CB or to put the CB bands to use in their business. In most households involved with amateur radio there is only one operator (generally the husband), whereas CB allows all members of a family to take part. Lady operators have established a very strong presence on CB — far more so than on the amateur bands — and contacts made have not always been restricted to radio topics: stories of marriages, divorces and 'dates' are commonplace — and that doesn't happen with amateur radio! There is a good case for both types of radio to co-exist because of their essential differences.

The Radio Regulatory Division of the Department of Trade and Industry publishes a series of Information Sheets about Citizens' Band radio in Great Britain. These are obtainable from their offices at Waterloo Bridge House, Waterloo Road, London SE1 8UA. The information which follows has been extracted from these leaflets and is published by permission of the DTI. Space permits only a very brief précis:

... One licence (present cost £10) covers three sets and more than one licence may be held. Apply at Post Offices. Licences are valid for one year and then renewable. They may be revoked if holders do not comply with the licence requirements.

... Licences are required even if persons confine their involvement to reception only.

... Only sets meeting the standard performance specifications are allowed. These carry marks (CB 27/81) for 27 MHz and (CB 934/81) for 934 MHz.

... No callsigns are officially issued and users are free to choose their own if they wish. There is no guarantee that other users will not have the same callsigns.

... Licensees must be aged fourteen years or over. Persons below that age may operate only under supervision. Non-licensed persons may also use CB equipment under the supervision of a licence holder.

... Transceivers may be used with accessories such as pre-amplifiers and attenuators but not those which increase trans-mitter power such as linear amplifiers (sometimes known as 'burners').

... Powers allowed are 4 watts at 27 MHz and 8 watts at 934 MHz.

... Coded transmissions (*eg* morse code and computer signals) are not allowed but CB language such as the 'Ten Code' is permissible. No music may be transmitted.

... Business use is allowed but no advertizing of goods or services is permissible.

... Authorized QRGs are 27.60125 to 27.99125 MHz in forty channels and 934.0125 to 934.9625 MHz in twenty channels. It is illegal to install or use CB equipment capable of transmitting outside these bands or on modes other than FM, which is the only legal mode allowed. AM and SSB are prohibited because of the increased dangers of interference to other radio users.

... The present frequency allocations may be altered if CEPT proposals for a European standard are brought into use. In these circumstances, the UK band on HF would be 26.96 to 27.41 MHz.

... British standard equipment may not normally be used at present in other countries.

... No-one has any preferential right to use a particular channel.

... There are restrictions on the size of antennas and restrictions on power for antennas more than 7 m (23 ft) above ground level. Erection of antennas is subject to local planning regulations.

... The DTI will take action against licence abuses but will not investigate complaints of QRM caused to non-radio equipment such as computers.

... A Code of Practice has been drawn up by the DTI, national CB groups, the Parliamentary CB Working Party and representatives of industry. The Code does not have the force of law but its adoption by operators is recommended. Amongst other things, it establishes an emergency monitoring system on Channel 9 27.68125 MHz) which should be kept clear of all non-emergency communications. It nominates Channel 14 (27.73125 MHz) as a calling channel from which operators should move once they have established contact. Channel 19 (27.78125 MHz) is allocated to travellers on main roads, who should avoid long conversations which will affect other users. The Code also makes the point that the use of CB slang is not necessary and plain language is just as effective.

What does the future hold in store for CB radio? The DTI publications do not make any predictions apart from explaining the proposals by the Conference of European Posts and Telecommunications Administrations referred to earlier. There is no doubt that the CB 'boom' has passed, not only in the USA and Great Britain but also in virtually every other country involved. My own view is that the decline will continue in the short term. Changing to a European standard is to be welcomed in view of the present haphazard licensing system but it will mean that much of the equipment currently available will become obsolete. Many European countries will have to switch to FM instead of AM which they now use, whilst British CB fans will have a new range of frequencies. The success of these changes will depend on the willingness of manufacturers to cater for the new market and many of them remain sceptical of the value of such investment.

CB radio could be said to fall into two categories: business/ information and hobby activity. There will remain a need for business users and road transport to continue to exchange information by radio and communication will be most valuable when the sunspot count is low and QRM from DX stations is non-existent. The major decline is most likely to be in the 'hobby' activities because of the impact of other, newer aspects of electronics. Many of the CB radio clubs and magazines which were in evidence a few years ago have since folded up and there are few new ones to take their places. We could see an upturn in interest as the next sunspot peak approaches at the start of the next decade but this is by no means certain. By then it could well be difficult to obtain CB radio equipment and to get it repaired when required.

Appendix 1

ITU *block callsign allocations*

A2A – A2Z	Botswana	DSA – DTZ	Korea (South)
A3A – A3Z	Tonga	DUA – DZZ	Philippines
A4A – A4Z	Oman	EAA – EHZ	Spain
A5A – A5Z	Bhutan	EIA – EJZ	Ireland
A6A – A6Z	United Arab Emirates	EKA – EKZ	USSR
A7A – A7Z	Qatar	ELA – ELZ	Liberia
A8A – A8Z	Liberia	EMA – EOZ	USSR
A9A – A9Z	Bahrain	EPA – EQZ	Iran
AAA – ALZ	USA	ERA – ESZ	USSR
AMA – AOZ	Spain	ETA – ETZ	Ethiopia
APA – ASZ	Pakistan	EUA – EZZ	USSR
ATA – AWZ	India	FAA – FZZ	France & French
AXA – AXZ	Australia		territories
AYA – AZZ	Argentina	GAA – GZZ	United Kingdom
BAA – BZZ	China	H2A – H2Z	Cyprus
C2A – C2Z	Nauru	H3A – H3Z	Panama
C3A – C3Z	Andorra	H4A – H4Z	Solomon Islands
C4A – C4Z	Cyprus	H5A – H5Z	Bophuthatswana
C5A – C5Z	Gambia	H6A – H7Z	Nicaragua
C6A – C6Z	Bahamas	H8A – H9Z	Panama
C8A – C9Z	Mozambique	HAA – HAZ	Hungary
CAA – CEZ	Chile	HBA – HBZ	Switzerland
CFA – CKZ	Canada	HCA – HDZ	Ecuador
CLA – CMZ	Cuba	HEA – HEZ	Switzerland
CNA – CNZ	Morocco	HFA – HFZ	Poland
COA – COZ	Cuba	HGA – HGZ	Hungary
CPA – CPZ	Bolivia	HHA – HHZ	Haiti
CQA – CUZ	Portugal	HIA – HIZ	Dominican Republic
CVA – CXZ	Uruguay	HJA – HKZ	Colombia
CYA – CZZ	Canada	HLA – HLZ	Korea (South)
D2A – D3Z	Angola	HMA – HMZ	Korea (North)
D4A – D4Z	Cape Verde	HNA – HNZ	Iraq
D5A – D5Z	Liberia	HOA – HPZ	Panama
D6A – D6Z	Comoros	HQA – HRZ	Honduras
D7A – D9Z	Korea (South)	HSA – HSZ	Thailand
DAA – DRZ	Fed Rep of Germany	HTA – HTZ	Nicaragua

HUA – HUZ	El Salvador	SAA – SMZ	Sweden
HVA – HVZ	Vatican	SNA – SRZ	Poland
HWA – HYZ	France	SSA – SSM	Egypt
HZA – HZZ	Saudi Arabia	SSN – STZ	Sudan
IAA – IZZ	Italy	SUA – SUZ	Egypt
J2A – J2Z	Djibouti	SVA – SZZ	Greece
J3A – J3Z	Grenada	T2A – T2Z	Tuvalu
J4A – J4Z	Greece	T3A – T3Z	Kiribati
J5A – J5Z	Guinea-Bissau	T4A – T4Z	Cuba
J6A – J6Z	St Lucia	T5A – T5Z	Somalia
J7A – J7Z	Dominica	T6A – T6Z	Afghanistan
J8A – J8Z	St Vincent &	T7A – T7Z	San Marino
	Grenadines	TAA – TCZ	Turkey
JAA – JSZ	Japan	TDA – TDZ	Guatemala
JTA – JVZ	Mongolia	TEA – TEZ	Costa Rica
JWA – JXZ	Norway	TFA – TFZ	Iceland
JYA – JYZ	Jordan	TGA – TGZ	Guatemala
JZA – JZZ	Indonesia	THA – THZ	France
KAA – KZZ	USA	TIA – TIZ	Costa Rica
L2A – L9Z	Argentina	TJA – TJZ	Cameroon
LAA – LNZ	Norway	TKA – TKZ	France
LOA – LWZ	Argentina	TLA – TLZ	Central African
LXA – LXZ	Luxembourg		Republic
LYA – LYZ	USSR	TMA – TMZ	France
LZA – LZZ	Bulgaria	TNA – TNZ	Congo
MAA – MZZ	United Kingdom	TOA – TQZ	France
NAA – NZZ	USA	TRA – TRZ	Gabon
OAA – OCZ	Peru	TSA – TSZ	Tunisia
ODA – ODZ	Lebanon	TTA – TTZ	Chad
OEA – OEZ	Austria	TUA – TUZ	Ivory Coast
OFA – OJZ	Finland	TVA – TXZ	France
OKA – OMZ	Czechoslovakia	TYA – TYZ	Benin
ONA – OTZ	Belgium	TZA – TZZ	Mali
OUA – OZZ	Denmark	UAA – UZZ	USSR
P2A – P2Z	Papua New Guinea	V2A – V2Z	Antigua & Barbuda
P3A – P3Z	Cyprus	V3A – V3Z	Belize
P4A – P4Z	Netherlands Antilles	V4A – V4Z	St Kitts
P5A – P9Z	Korea (North)	V8A – V8Z	Brunei
PAA – PIZ	Netherlands	VAA – VGZ	Canada
PJA – PJZ	Netherlands Antilles	VHA – VNZ	Australia
PKA – POZ	Indonesia	VOA – VOZ	Canada
PPA – PYZ	Brazil	VPA – VSZ	British
PZA – PZZ	Surinam		Commonwealth
RAA – RZZ	USSR	VTA – VWZ	India
S2A – S3Z	Bangladesh	VXA – VYZ	Canada
S6A – S6Z	Singapore	VZA – VZZ	Australia
S7A – S7Z	Seychelles	WAA – WZZ	USA
S8A – S8Z	Transkei	XAA – XIZ	Mexico
S9A – S9Z	Sao Tome and Principe	XJZ – XOZ	Canada

XPA – XPZ	Denmark	3ZA – 3ZZ	Poland
XQA – XRZ	Chile	4AA – 4CZ	Mexico
XSA – XSZ	China	4DA – 4IZ	Philippines
XTA – XTZ	Burkina Faso	4JA – 4LZ	USSR
XUA – XUZ	Kampuchea	4MA – 4MZ	Venezuela
XVA – XVZ	Vietnam	4NA – 4OZ	Yugoslavia
XWA – XWZ	Laos	4PA – 4SZ	Sri Lanka
XXA – XXZ	Portugal	4TA – 4TZ	Peru
XYA – XZZ	Burma	4UA – 4UZ	United Nations
Y2A – Y9Z	German Democratic		Organization
	Republic	4VA – 4VZ	Haiti
YAA – YAZ	Afghanistan	4WA – 4WZ	Yemen Arab Republic
YBA – YHZ	Indonesia	4XA – 4XZ	Israel
YIA – YIZ	Iraq	4ZA – 4ZZ	Israel
YJA – YJZ	Vanuatu	5AA – 5AZ	Libya
YKA – YKZ	Syria	5BA – 5BZ	Cyprus
YLA – YLZ	USSR	5CA – 5GZ	Morocco
YMA – YMZ	Turkey	5HA – 5IZ	Tanzania
YNA – YNZ	Nicaragua	5JA – 5KZ	Colombia
YOA – YRZ	Romania	5LA – 5MZ	Liberia
YSA – YSZ	El Salvador	5NA – 5OZ	Nigeria
YTA – YUZ	Yugoslavia	5PA – 5QZ	Denmark
YVA – YYZ	Venezuela	5RA – 5SZ	Madagascar
YZA – YZZ	Yugoslavia	5TA – 5TZ	Mauritania
Z2A – Z2Z	Zimbabwe	5UA – 5UZ	Niger
ZAA – ZAZ	Albania	5VA – 5VZ	Togo
ZBA – ZJZ	British	5WA – 5WZ	Western Samoa
	Commonwealth	5XA – 5XZ	Uganda
ZKA – ZMZ	New Zealand	5YA – 5ZZ	Kenya
ZNA – ZOZ	British	6AA – 6BZ	Egypt
	Commonwealth	6CA – 6CZ	Syria
ZPA – ZPZ	Paraguay	6DA – 6JZ	Mexico
ZQA – ZQZ	British	6KA – 6NZ	Korea (South)
	Commonwealth	6OA – 6OZ	Somalia
ZRA – ZUZ	South Africa	6PA – 6SZ	Pakistan
ZVA – ZZZ	Brazil	6TA – 6UZ	Sudan
2AA – 2ZZ	United Kingdom	6VA – 6WZ	Senegal
3AA – 3AZ	Monaco	6XA – 6XZ	Madagascar
3BA – 3BZ	Mauritius	6YA – 6YZ	Jamaica
3CA – 3CZ	Equatorial Guinea	6ZA – 6ZZ	Liberia
3DA – 3DM	Swaziland	7AA – 7IZ	Indonesia
3DN – 3DZ	Fiji	7JA – 7NZ	Japan
3EA – 3FZ	Panama	7OA – 7OZ	Yemen People's Dem
3GA – 3GZ	Chile		Republic
3HA – 3UZ	China	7PA – 7PZ	Lesotho
3VA – 3VZ	Tunisia	7QA – 7QZ	Malawi
3WA – 3WZ	Vietnam	7RA – 7RZ	Algeria
3XA – 3XZ	Republic of Guinea	7SA – 7SZ	Sweden
3YA – 3YZ	Norway	7TA – 7YZ	Algeria

7ZA – 7ZZ	Saudi Arabia	9GA – 9GZ	Ghana
8AA – 8IZ	Indonesia	9HA – 9HZ	Malta
8JA – 8NZ	Japan	9IA – 9JZ	Zambia
8OA – 8OZ	Botswana	9KA – 9KZ	Kuwait
8PA – 8PZ	Barbados	9LA – 9LZ	Sierra Leone
8QA – 8QZ	Maldives	9MA – 9MZ	Malaysia
8RA – 8RZ	Guyana	9NA – 9NZ	Nepal
8SA – 8SZ	Sweden	9OA – 9TZ	Zaire
8TA – 8YZ	India	9UA – 9UZ	Burundi
8ZA – 8ZZ	Saudi Arabia	9VA – 9VZ	Singapore
9AA – 9AZ	San Marino	9WA – 9WZ	Malaysia
9BA – 9DZ	Iran	9XA – 9XZ	Rwanda
9EA – 9FZ	Ethiopia	9YA – 9ZZ	Trinidad & Tobago

Appendix 2

Short wave radio countries, prefixes, continents, CQ zones, ITU zones

Country	Prefix	Continent	CQ zone	ITU zone
Afghanistan	YA	AS	21	40
Agalega Is.	3B6/7	AF	39	53
Aland Is.	OHØ	EU	15	18
Alaska	KL7	NA	1	1–2
Albania	ZA	EU	15	28
Algeria	7X	AF	33	37
Amsterdam & St Paul Is.	FT8Z	AF	39	68
Andaman & Nicobar Is.	VU	AS	26	49
Andorra	C3	EU	14	27
Angola	D2	AF	36	52
Anguilla	VP2E	NA	8	11
Antarctica	Various	SA/OC/AF	12,13,29,30, 32,38,39	67,69–74
Antigua	V2A	NA	8	11
Argentina	LU	SA	13	14,16
Armenia	UG	AS	21	29
Ascension Is.	ZD8	AF	36	66
Auckland & Campbell Is.	ZL9	OC	32	60
Australia	VK	OC	29,30	55,58,59
Austria	OE	EU	15	28
Aves Is.	YV	NA	8	11
Azerbaijan	UD	AS	21	29
Azores Is.	CU	EU	14	36
Bahamas	C6	NA	8	11
Bahrain	A9	AS	21	39
Baker & Howland Is.	KH1	OC	31	61,62
Balearic Is.	EA6	EU	14	37
Bangladesh	S2	AS	22	41
Barbados	8P	NA	8	11
Belau	KC6	OC	27	65

Country	Prefix	Continent	CQ zone	ITU zone
Belgium	ON	EU	14	27
Belize	V3	NA	7	11
Benin	TY	AF	35	46
Bermuda	VP9	NA	5	11
Bhutan	A5	AS	22	41
Bolivia	CP	SA	10	12,14
Botswana	A2	AF	38	57
Bouvet Is.	3Y	AF	38	67
Brazil	PY	SA	11	12,13,15
Brunei	V85	OC	28	54
Bulgaria	LZ	EU	20	28
Burkina Faso	XT	AF	35	46
Burma	XZ	AS	26	49
Burundi	9U	AF	36	52
Byelorussia	UC	EU	16	29
Cameroun	TJ	AF	36	47
Canada	VE	NA	1–5	2–4,9,75
Canary Is.	EA8	AF	33	36
Cape Verde Is.	D4	AF	35	46
Cayman Is.	ZF	NA	8	11
Central African Rep.	TL	AF	36	47
Ceuta & Melilla	EA9	AF	33	37
Chad	TT	AF	36	47
Chagos Is.	VQ9	AF	39	41
Chatham Is.	ZL7	OC	32	60
Chile	CE	SA	12	14,16
China	BY	AS	23,24	32,42–44
Christmas Is.	VK9X	OC	29	54
Clipperton Is.	FO	NA	7	10
Cocos Is.	TI9	NA	7	11
Cocos-Keeling Is.	VK9Y	OC	29	54
Colombia	HK	SA	9	12
Comoro Is.	D68	AF	39	53
Congo	TN	AF	36	47,52
Cook Is., North	ZK1	OC	32	62
Cook Is., South	ZK1	OC	32	62
Corsica	TK	EU	15	28
Costa Rica	TI	NA	7	11
Crete	SV9	EU	20	28
Crozet Is.	FT8W	AF	39	68
Cuba	CO	NA	8	11
Cyprus	5B	AS	20	39
Cyprus, sovereign bases	ZC4	AS	20	39
Czechoslovakia	OK	EU	15	28
Denmark	OZ	EU	14	18

Country	Prefix	Continent	CQ zone	ITU zone
Desecheo Is.	KP5	NA	8	11
Djibouti	J28	AF	37	48
Dodecanese Is.	SV5	EU	20	28
Dominica	J7	NA	8	11
Dominican Rep.	HI	NA	8	11
Easter Is.	CEØ	SA	12	63
Ecuador	HC	SA	10	12
Egypt	SU	AF	34	38
Eire	EI	EU	14	27
El Salvador	YS	NA	7	11
England	G	EU	14	27
Equatorial Guinea	3C	AF	36	47
Estonia	UR	EU	15	29
Ethiopia	ET	AF	37	48
Falkland Is.	VP8	SA	13	16
Faroe Is.	OY	EU	14	18
Fernando de Noronha	PYØ	SA	11	13
Fiji	3D2	OC	32	56
Finland	OH	EU	15	18
France	F	EU	14	27
Franz Josef Land	UA1	EU	40	75
French Guiana	FY	SA	9	12
French Polynesia	FO	OC	32	63
French St Martin	FS	NA	8	11
Gabon	TR	AF	36	52
Galapagos Is.	HC8	SA	10	12
Gambia	C5	AF	35	46
Georgia	UF	AS	21	29
German Democratic Rep.	Y	EU	14	28
German Federal Rep.	DL	EU	14	28
Ghana	9G	AF	35	46
Gibraltar	ZB2	EU	14	37
Glorieuses Is.	FR/G	AF	39	53
Greece	SV	EU	20	28
Greenland	OX	NA	40	5,75
Grenada	J3	NA	8	11
Guadeloupe	FG	NA	8	11
Guam	KH2	OC	27	64
Guantanamo Bay	KG4	NA	8	11
Guatemala	TG	NA	7	11
Guernsey	GU	EU	14	27
Guinea-Bissau	J5	AF	35	46
Guinea	3X	AF	35	46
Guyana	8R	SA	9	12

Country	Prefix	Continent	CQ zone	ITU zone
Haiti	HH	NA	8	11
Hawaiian Is.	KH6	OC	31	61
Heard Is.	VKØ	AF	39	68
Honduras	HR	NA	7	11
Hong Kong	VS6	AS	24	44
Hungary	HA	EU	15	28
Iceland	TF	EU	40	17
India	VU	AS	22	41
Indonesia	YB	OC	28	51,54
Iran	EP	AS	21	40
Iraq	YI	AS	21	39
Isle of Man	GD	EU	14	27
Israel	4X	AS	20	39
Italy	I	EU	15	28
ITU, Geneva	4U1	EU	14	27
Ivory Coast	TU	AF	35	46
Jamaica	6Y	NA	8	11
Jan Mayen Is.	JX	EU	40	18
Japan	JA	AS	25	44,45
Jersey	GJ	EU	14	27
Johnston Is.	KH3	OC	31	61
Jordan	JY	AS	20	39
Juan de Nova, Europa Is.	FR/J	AF	39	53
Juan Fernandez Arch.	CEØ	SA	12	14
Kaliningradsk	UA2	EU	15	29
Kampuchea	XU	AS	26	49
Kazakh	UL	AS	17	30,31
Kenya	5Z	AF	37	48
Kerguelen Is.	FT8X	AF	39	68
Kermadec Is.	ZL8	OC	32	60
Kingman Reef	KH5K	OC	31	61
Kirghiz	UM	AS	17	30,31
Kiribati, Central	T32	OC	31	62
Kiribati, East	T31	OC	31	61,63
Kiribati, West	T3Ø	OC	31	65
Korea	HL	AS	25	44
Kure Is.	KH7	OC	31	61
Kuwait	9K2	AS	21	39
Laccadive Is.	VU	AS	22	41
Laos	XW	AS	26	49
Latvia	UQ	EU	15	29
Lebanon	OD	AS	20	39
Lesotho	7P	AF	38	57
Liberia	EL	AF	35	46
Libya	5A	AF	34	38

Country	Prefix	Continent	CQ zone	ITU zone
Liechtenstein	HBØ	EU	14	28
Lithuania	UP	EU	15	29
Lord Howe Is.	VK	OC	30	60
Luxembourg	LX	EU	14	27
Macao	XX9	AS	24	44
Macquarie Is.	VKØ	OC	30	60
Madagascar	5R	AF	39	53
Madeira	CT3	AF	33	36
Malawi	7Q	AF	37	53
Malaysia, East	9M6	OC	28	54
Malaysia, West	9M2	AS	28	54
Maldives	8Q	AS/AF	22,39	41
Mali	TZ	AF	35	46
Malpelo Is.	HKØ	SA	9	12
Malta	9H	EU	15	28
Mariana Is.	KHØ	OC	27	64
Market Reef	OJØ	EU	15	18
Marshall Is.	KX6	OC	31	65
Martinique	FM	NA	8	11
Mauritania	5T	AF	35	46
Mauritius	3B8	AF	39	53
Mayotte	FH8	AF	39	53
Mellish Reef	VK9	OC	30	56
Mexico	XE	NA	6	10
Micronesia	KC6	OC	27	65
Midway Is.	KH4	OC	31	61
Minami Torishima	JD	OC	27	90
Moldavia	UO	EU	16	29
Monaco	3A	EU	14	27
Mongolia	JT	AS	23	32,33
Montserrat	VP2M	NA	8	11
Morocco	CN	AF	33	37
Mount Athos	SV	EU	20	28
Mozambique	C9	AF	37	53
Namibia	ZS3	AF	38	57
Nauru	C2	OC	31	65
Navassa Is.	KP1	NA	8	11
Nepal	9N	AS	22	41
Netherlands	PA	EU	14	27
Netherlands Antilles, Leeward•	PJ	NA	8	11
Netherlands Antilles, Windward•	PJ	SA	9	11
New Caledonia	FK	OC	32	56
New Zealand	ZL	OC	32	60
Nicaragua	YN	NA	7	11
Niger	5U	AF	35	46

Country	Prefix	Continent	CQ zone	ITU zone
Nigeria	5N	AF	35	46
Niue	ZK2	OC	32	62
Norfolk Is.	VK9N	OC	32	60
Northern Ireland	GI	EU	14	27
Norway	LA	EU	14	18
Ogasawara Is.	JD	AS	27	45
Oman	A4	AS	21	39
Pagalu Is.	3CØ	AF	36	52
Pakistan	AP	AS	21	41
Palmyra & Jarvis Is.	KH5	OC	31	61,62
Panama	HP	NA	7	11
Papua New Guinea	P29	OC	28	51
Paraguay	ZP	SA	11	14
Peru	OA	SA	10	12
Philippine Is.	DU	OC	27	50
Pitcairn Is.	VR6	OC	32	63
Poland	SP	EU	15	28
Portugal	CT1	EU	14	37
Prince Edward & Marion Is.	ZS2	AF	38	57
Puerto Rico	KP4	NA	8	11
Qatar	A7	AS	21	39
Red Sea Islands	Various	AS	21	39
Reunion Is.	FR	AF	39	53
Revilla Gigedo Is.	XF4	NA	6	10
Rodriguez Is.	3B9	AF	39	53
Romania	YO	EU	20	28
Russia, Asiatic	UA9/Ø	AS	17–19,23	20–26,30–35
Russia, European	UA	EU	16	19,20,29,30
Rwanda	9X5	AF	36	52
Sable Is.	CY9	NA	5	9
St Helena	ZD7	AF	36	66
St Kitts	V4	NA	8	11
St Lucia	J6	NA	8	11
St Paul Is.	CYØ	NA	5	9
St Peter & St Paul Rocks	PYØ	SA	11	13
St Pierre & Miquelon	FP	NA	5	9
St Vincent	J8	NA	8	11
Samoa, American	KH8	OC	32	62
Samoa, Western	5W	OC	32	62
San Andres Is.	HKØ	NA	7	11
San Felix Is.	CEØX	SA	12	14
San Marino	T7	EU	15	28
Sao Tome & Principe	S9	AF	36	47

Country	Prefix	Continent	CQ zone	ITU zone
Sardinia	IS	EU	15	28
Saudi Arabia	HZ	AS	21	39
Scotland	GM	EU	14	27
Senegal	6W	AF	35	46
Seychelles	S7	AF	39	53
Sierra Leone	9L	AF	35	46
Singapore	9V	AS	28	54
Solomon Is.	H4	OC	28	51
Somalia	T5	AF	37	48
South Africa	ZS	AF	38	57
South Georgia	VP8	SA	13	73
South Orkney Is.	VP8	SA	13	73
South Sandwich Is.	VP8	SA	13	73
South Shetland Is.	VP8	SA	13	73
Spain	EA	EU	14	37
Spratly Is.	1S	AS	26	50
Sri Lanka	4S	AS	22	41
Sudan	ST	AF	34	47,48
Sudan, Southern	STØ	AF	34	47,48
Surinam	PZ	SA	9	12
Svalbard Archipelago	JW	EU	40	18
Swaziland	3D	AF	38	57
Sweden	SM	EU	14	18
Switzerland	HB9	EU	14	28
Syria	YK	AS	20	39
Tadzhik	UJ	AS	17	30
Taiwan	BV	AS	24	44
Tanzania	5H	AF	37	53
Thailand	HS	AS	26	49
Togo	5V	AF	35	46
Tokelau Is.	ZK3	OC	31	62
Tonga	A3	OC	32	62
Trinidad & Tobago	9Y	SA	9	11
Trindade Is.	PYØ	SA	11	15
Tristan da Cunha	ZD9	AF	38	66
Tromelin Is.	FR/T	AF	39	53
Tunisia	3V	AF	33	37
Turkey	TA	EU/AS	20	39
Turkoman	UH	AS	17	30
Turks & Caicos Is.	VP5	NA	8	11
Tuvalu	T2	OC	31	65
Uganda	5X	AF	37	48
Ukraine	UB	EU	16	29
United Arab Emirates	A6	AS	21	39
UN New York	4U1	NA	5	8

Country	Prefix	Continent	CQ zone	ITU zone
Uruguay	CX	SA	13	14
USA	W	NA	3–5	6–8
Uzbek	UI	AS	17	30
Vanuatu	YJ	OC	32	56
Vatican City	HV	EU	15	28
Venezuela	YV	SA	9	12
Vietnam	XV	AS	26	49
Virgin Is., American	KP2	NA	8	11
Virgin Is., British	VP2V	NA	8	11
Wake Is.	KH9	OC	31	65
Wales	GW	EU	14	27
Wallis & Futuna Is.	FW	OC	32	62
Willis Is.	VK9	OC	30	55
Yemen	4W	AS	21	39
Yemen, South	7O	AS	21,37	39
Yugoslavia	YU	EU	15	28
Zaire	9Q	AF	36	52
Zambia	9J	AF	36	53
Zimbabwe	Z2	AF	38	53

Continents: AF = Africa; AS = Asia; EU = Europe;
        NA = North America; SA = South America; OC = Oceania.

• Netherlands Antilles (Windward Group) consists of Aruba, Bonaire and Curacao. The other islands are in the Leeward Group (Sint Maarten, *etc*).

Appendix 3

Amateur radio prefixes and standard numerals (where relevant)

(Referred to in chapter 4)

PX	No.	Country	PX	No.	Country
A2	2	Botswana	C9		Mozambique
A3	5	Tonga	CE		Chile
A4		Sultanate of Oman	CE9		Antarctica,
A5	1	Bhutan			Chilean bases
A6	1	United Arab Emirates	CE9		South Shetland Is.
A7	1	Qatar	CEØ		Easter Is.
A9	2	Bahrain	CEØ		Desventurados Is.
AA–AG		USA	CEØ		Juan Fernandez Is.
AH1		Baker & Howland Is.	CM		Cuba
AH2		Guam	CN		Morocco
AH3		Johnston Is.	CO		Cuba
AH4		Midway Is.	CP		Bolivia
AH5		Palmyra & Jarvis Is.	CT1		Portugal
AH5K		Kingman Reef	CT3		Madeira Is.
AH6		Hawaii	CT4		Portugal
AH7		Kure Is.	CU		Azores Is.
AH8		American Samoa	CX		Uruguay
AH9		Wake Is.	CY9		Sable Is.
AHØ		Northern Mariana Is.	CYØ		St Paul Is.
AI–AK		USA	D2		Angola
AL7		Alaska	D4	4	Cape Verde Is.
AM–AO		Spain	D6	8	Comoro Is.
AP	2	Pakistan	DA–DL		Western Germany
BV		Taiwan	DU		Philippine Is.
BY		China	EA1–5		Spain
C2	1	Nauru	EA6		Balearic Is.
C3	1	Andorra	EA7		Spain
C5	3	Gambia	EA8		Canary Is.
C6		Bahamas	EA9		Ceuta & Melilla

PX	No.	Country	PX	No.	Country
EC6		Balearic Is.	HC		Ecuador
EC8		Canary Is.	HC8		Galapagos Is.
EC9		Ceuta & Melilla	HG		Hungary
EI		Ireland	HH		Haiti
EL		Liberia	HI		Dominican Republic
EP		Iran	HK		Colombia
ET	3	Ethiopia	HKØ		San Andres Is.
F–FE		France	HKØ		Malpelo Is.
FG		Guadeloupe	HL–HM		Korea
FH		Mayotte	HP		Panama
FK	8	New Caledonia	HR		Honduras
FM		Martinique	HS	1	Thailand
FO	8	French Polynesia	HT		Nicaragua
FOØX		Clipperton Is.	HV		Vatican
FP		St Pierre & Miquelon	HZ	1	Saudi Arabia
FR		Reunion Is.	I–IF		Italy
FR		Glorioso Is. (sign /G)	IG	9	Pelagian Islands
FR		Juan de Nova (sign /J)	IH	9	Pantellaria Is.
FR		Tromelin Is. (sign /T)	IJ–IL	7	Italy
FS		French Saint Martin	IM	Ø	Sardinia
FT8W		Crozet Is.	IN	3	Trentino-Alto Adige
FT8X		Kerguelen Is.	IO		Italy
FT8Y		Adelie Land	IP–IR		Italy
FT8Z		New Amsterdam Is.	IS	Ø	Sardinia
FW		Wallis & Futuna Is.	IT	9	Sicily
FY		French Guiana	IV	3	Friuli-Venezia Giulia
G		England	IX	1	Aosta Valley
GB		Great Britain	J2	8	Djibouti
GD		Isle of Man	J2		Abu Ail (stns sign /A)
GI		Northern Ireland	J3	7	Grenada
GJ		Jersey	J5		Guinea-Bissau
GM		Scotland	J6		St Lucia
GU		Guernsey	J7	3	Dominica
GW		Wales	J8		St Vincent
H4	4	Solomon Is.	JA		Japan
H5		Bophuthatswana	JD	1	Minami Torishima
HA		Hungary	JD	1	Ogasawara Is.
HB9		Switzerland	JE–JS		Japan
HBØ		Liechtenstein	JT		Mongolia

PX	No.	Country	PX	No.	Country
JW		Svalbard Is.	NA–NZ		(As for KA–KZ minus
JX		Jan Mayen Is.			KC4,KC6,KG4,KG6)
JY		Jordan	OA		Peru
K		USA	OD	5	Lebanon
KA–KG		USA	OE		Austria
KC4		Antarctica (USA bases)	OH		Finland
KC6		West Caroline Is.	OHØ		Aland Is.
KC6		East Caroline Is.	OJØ		Market Reef
KG4		Guantanamo Bay	OK		Czechoslovakia
KG6		Guam	ON		Belgium
KG6		Northern Mariana Is.	OX		Greenland
KH1		Baker & Howland Is.	OY		Faroe Is.
KH2		Guam	OZ		Denmark
KH3		Johnston Is.	P2	9	Papua New Guinea
KH4		Midway Is.	P4		Aruba
KH5		Palmyra & Jarvis Is.	PA		Netherlands
KH5K		Kingman Reef	PI		Netherlands
KH6		Hawaii	PJ1–4		Neth. Antilles, Windward
KH7		Kure Is.	PJ5–8		Neth. Antilles, Leeward
KH8		American Samoa	PJ9		Neth. Antilles, Windward
KH9		Wake Is.	PP–PW		Brazil
KHØ		Northern Mariana Is.	PY		Brazil
KI–KK		USA	PYØF		Fernando de Noronha Is.
KL7		Alaska	PYØS		St Peter & St Paul Rocks
KM–KO		USA	PYØT		Trindade Is.
KP1		Navassa Is.	PZ		Surinam
KP2		US Virgin Is.	RA–RZ		(As for UA–UZ)
KP4		Puerto Rico	S2		Bangladesh
KP5		Desecheo Is.	S7	9	Seychelles
KQ–KZ		USA	S8		Transkei
KV4		US Virgin Is.	S9		Sao Tome & Principe Is.
KX6		Marshall Is.	SK–SM		Sweden
LA		Norway	SP		Poland
LU		Argentina	ST	2	Sudan
LU		South Orkney Is.	STØ		Southern Sudan
LU		South Sandwich Is.	SU	1	Egypt
LU		South Shetland Is.	SV		Greece
LX		Luxembourg	SV		Mount Athos (stns sign /A)
LZ		Bulgaria	SV5		Dodecanese Is.

PX	No.	Country	PX	No.	Country
SV9		Crete	UP		Lithuania
T2		Tuvalu	UQ		Latvia
T3∅		Western Kiribati	UR		Estonia
T31		Central Kiribati	UT		Ukraine
T32		Eastern Kiribati	UV1,3,4,6		USSR, European
T5		Somalia	UV9–∅		USSR, Asian
T7	7	San Marino	UW1,3,4,6		USSR, European
TA		Turkey	UW9–∅		USSR, Asian
TF		Iceland	UY		Ukraine
TG		Guatemala	UZ1,3,4,6		USSR, European
TI		Costa Rica	UZ9–∅		USSR, Asian
TI9		Cocos Is.	V2		Antigua & Barbuda
TJ	1	Cameroun	V3		Belize
TK		Corsica	V4	4	St Kitts
TL	8	Central African Rep.	V8	5	Brunei
TN	8	Congo	VE		Canada
TR	8	Gabon	VK		Australia
TT	8	Chad	VK9L		Lord Howe Is.
TU		Ivory Coast	VK9M		Mellish Reef
TY		Benin	VK9N		Norfolk Is.
TZ		Mali	VK9X		Christmas Is.
UA1		USSR, European	VK9Y		Cocos-Keeling Is.
UA1O-P		Franz Josef Land	VK9Z		Willis Is.
UA2		Kaliningradsk	VK∅		Heard Is.
UA3-4		USSR, European	VK∅		Macquarie Is.
UA6		USSR, European	VK∅		Antarctica, Australian
UA9–∅		USSR, Asian	VO1		Newfoundland, Canada
UB		Ukraine	VO2		Labrador, Canada
UC		Byelorussia	VP2E		Anguilla
UD		Azerbaijan	VP2M		Montserrat
UF		Georgia	VP2V		British Virgin Is.
UG		Armenia	VP5		Turks & Caicos Is.
UH		Turkoman	VP8		British Antarctica
UI		Uzbek	VP8		Falkland Is.
UJ		Tadzhik	VP8		South Georgia
UL		Kazakh	VP8		South Orkney Is.
UM		Kirghiz	VP8		South Sandwich Is.
UN		Karelo-Finnish Rep.	VP8		South Shetland Is.
UO		Moldavia	VP9		Bermuda

PX	No.	Country	PX	No.	Country
VQ9		Chagos Is.	ZF		Cayman Is.
VR6		Pitcairn Is.	ZK1		North Cook Is.
VS6		Hong Kong	ZK1		South Cook Is.
VU	2	India	ZK2		Niue
VU		Andaman & Nicobar Is.	ZK3		Tokelau Is.
			ZL1-4		New Zealand
VU		Laccadive Is.	ZL7		Chatham Is.
VY1		Yukon, Canada	ZL8		Kermadec Is.
W		USA	ZL9		Campbell Is.
WA-WZ		(See KA-KZ minus KC4, KC6, KG4, KG6)	ZP		Paraguay
			ZS1-2		South Africa
XE		Mexico	ZS2MI		Marion Is.
XF4		Revilla Gigedo Is.	ZS3		Namibia
XP		Greenland	ZS4-6		South Africa
XT	2	Burkina Faso	1AØKM		Sovereign Military Order of Malta, Rome
XU		Kampuchea			
XV		Vietnam	1S	1	Spratly Is.
XW		Laos	1Z		Burma
XX	9	Macao	3A		Monaco
XZ		Burma	3B6		Agalega Islands
Y		Eastern Germany (GDR)	3B8		Mauritius
YA		Afghanistan	3B9		Rodriguez Is.
YB-YD		Indonesia	3C1		Equatorial Guinea
YI		Iraq	3CØ		Annobon Is. (Pagalu)
YJ	8	Vanuatu	3D2		Fiji
YK		Syria	3D6		Swaziland
YN		Nicaragua	3V	8	Tunisia
YO		Romania	3Y		Bouvet Is.
YS		El Salvador	4K1		Antarctica,USSR bases
YT-YU		Yugoslavia	4K1		S. Shetland,USSR bases
YV		Venezuela	4S	7	Sri Lanka
YVØ		Aves Is.	4U		UN Forces, Egypt
Z2		Zimbabwe	4U1UN		UN New York
ZA		Albania	4U1ITU		ITU, Geneva
ZB2		Gibraltar	4W		Yemen
ZC4		Cyprus (British bases)	4X		Israel
ZD7		St Helena	4Z		Israel
ZD8		Ascension Is.	5A		Libya
ZD9		Tristan da Cunha	5B	4	Cyprus

PX	No.	Country	PX	No.	Country
5H	3	Tanzania	8P	6	Barbados
5N		Nigeria	8Q	7	Maldive Is.
5R	8	Madagascar	8R	1	Guyana
5T	5	Mauritania	9G		Ghana
5V		Togo	9H		Malta
5W	1	Western Samoa	9J	2	Zambia
5X	5	Uganda	9K	2	Kuwait
5Z	4	Kenya	9L	1	Sierra Leone
6T	2	Sudan	9M2		Malaysia, Western
6W		Senegal	9M6,8		Malaysia, Eastern
6Y	5	Jamaica	9N	1	Nepal
7J	1	Okino Torishima	9Q	5	Zaire
7O		South Yemen	9U	5	Burundi
7P	8	Lesotho	9V	1	Singapore
7Q	7	Malawi	9X	5	Rwanda
7X		Algeria	9Y	4	Trinidad & Tobago

Appendix 4

Countries subdivided by call areas

(Referred to in chapter 4)

Some countries issue amateur radio callsigns which indicate not only the country in which the station is located but also the general geographical area. The numeral following the prefix is normally used though in isolated cases it is the first letter after the numeral which conveys this information. The examples given in this Appendix are only a selection of the countries involved and have been chosen because the countries may be classified as DX and are regularly heard.

Argentina

The first letter of the suffix indicates the location (*eg* LU1AZZ would be in Buenos Aires city).

A,B,C: Buenos Aires (city); D,E: Buenos Aires (province); F: Santa Fe; G: Chaco, Formosa; H: Cordoba; I: Misiones; J: Entre Rios; K: Tucuman; L: Corrientes; M: Mendoza; N: Santiago del Estero; O: Salta; P: San Juan; Q: San Luis; R: Catamarca; S: La Rioja; T: Jujuy; U: La Pampa; V: Rio Negro; W: Chubut; X: Santa Cruz, Tierra del Fuego; Y: Neuquen; Z: Argentinian bases in Antarctica.

Australia

VK1: Australian Capital Territory (Canberra); VK2: New South Wales; VK3: Victoria; VK4: Queensland; VK5: South Australia; VK6: Western Australia; VK7: Tasmania; VK8: Northern Territory; VK9: Lord Howe Is., Mellish Reef, Norfolk Is., Christmas Is., Cocos-Keeling Is., Willis Is.; VKØ Heard Is., Macquarie Is., Australian bases in Antarctica.

Bolivia

CP1: La Paz; CP2: Chuquisaca; CP3: Oruro; CP4: Potosi; CP5: Cochabamba; CP6: Santa Cruz; CP7: Tarija; CP8: Beni; CP9: Pando.

Canada

VE1: Nova Scotia, New Brunswick, Prince Edward Is.; VE2: Quebec; VE3: Ontario; VE4: Manitoba; VE5: Saskatchewan; VE6: Alberta; VE7: British Columbia; VE8: North West Territories; VO1: Newfoundland; VO2: Labrador; VY1: Yukon; CY9 (or VX9): Sable Is.; CYØ (or VYØ): St Paul Is.

Chile

CE1: Tacna, Tarapaca, Antofagasta, Atacama; CE2: Valparaiso, Aconcagua, Coquimbo; CE3: Santiago; CE4: O'Higgins, Colchagua, Curico, Talca, Maule, Linares; CE5: Concepcion, Bio Bio, Arauco, Malleco; CE6: Cautin, Valdivia, Osorno; CE7: Llanquihue, Chiloe, Aysen; CE8: Magallanes; CE9: Chilean bases in Antarctica; CEØ Easter Is., Juan Fernandez Is., Desventurados Is.

Costa Rica

TI2: San Jose; TI3: Cartago; TI4: Heredia; TI5: Alajuela; TI6: Limon; TI7: Peninsula de Nicoya; TI8: Puntarenas; TI9: Cocos Is.

Ecuador

HC1: Quito; HC2: Guayaquil; HC3: Loja; HC4: Esmeraldas, Portoviejo; HC5: Cuenca; HC6: Ambato; HC7: Ecuador este; HC8: Galapagos Is.

Greece

SV1: Athens; SV2: Northern Greece; SV3: Peleponesos; SV4: Central Greece; SV5: Dodecanese Islands; SV6: Epirus; SV7: North Greece; SV8: Greek islands; SV9: Crete; SVØ: Visiting amateurs.

Japan

In addition to the JA prefix, Japanese stations may also use JE to JS. JA1: Tokyo; JA2: Nagoya; JA3: Osaka; JA4: Hiroshima; JA5: Shikoku; JA6: Kyushu; JA7: Sendai; JA8: Hokkaido; JA9: Toyama; JAØ Niigata; JD1: Minami Torishima, Ogasawara Is.; JR6: Ryukyu Is.

Mexico

XE1: Central Mexico; XE2: Northern Mexico; XE3: Southern Mexico; XF4: Revilla Gigedo Is.

New Zealand

ZL1: Auckland district; ZL2: Wellington district; ZL3: Canterbury district; ZL4: Otago district; ZL5: New Zealand bases in Antarctica.

Peru

OA1: Tumbes, Piura, Lambayeque; OA2: La Libertad, Cayamarca; OA3: Ancash, Huanuco; OA4: Lima, Cerro de Pasco, Junin; OA5: Huancavelica, Ica, Ayacucho, Apurimac; OA6: Arequipa, Moquegua, Tacna; OA7: Cuzco, Madre de Dios, Puno; OA8: Loreto; OA9: Amazonas, San Martin.

South Africa

ZS1: Cape Province; ZS2: Cape Midland and Eastern Cape; ZS3: Namibia; ZS4: Orange Free State, North West Cape; ZS5: Natal; ZS6: Transvaal.

United States Of America

CAUTION: This information is given only as a general guide since stations who move from one call district to another retain the original callsign. In addition to W, the prefix might be K, N, or in the blocks also allocated to the USA.

W1: States of Connecticut, Maine, Massachusetts, New Hampshire, Rhode Island, Vermont.
W2: States of New York, New Jersey.
W3: States of Delaware, Maryland, Pennsylvania.
W4: States of Alabama, Florida, Georgia, Kentucky, North Carolina, South Carolina, Tennessee, Virginia.
W5: States of Arkansas, Louisiana, Mississippi, New Mexico, Oklahoma, Texas.
W6: State of California.
W7: States of Arizona, Idaho, Montana, Nevada, Oregon, Utah, Washington, Wyoming.
W8: States of Michigan, Ohio, West Virginia.
W9: States of Illinois, Indiana, Wisconsin.
WØ States of Colorado, Iowa, Kansas, Minnesota, Missouri, Nebraska, North Dakota, South Dakota.

Appendix 5

International Morse Code

Standard Letters

A	di-dah
B	dah-di-di-dit
C	dah-di-dah-dit
D	dah-di-dit
E	dit
F	di-di-dah-dit
G	dah-dah-dit
H	di-di-di-dit
I	di-dit
J	di-dah-dah-dah
K	dah-di-dah
L	di-dah-di-dit
M	dah-dah
N	dah-dit
O	dah-dah-dah
P	di-dah-dah-dit
Q	dah-dah-di-dah
R	di-dah-dit
S	di-di-dit
T	dah
U	di-di-dah
V	di-di-di-dah
W	di-dah-dah
X	dah-di-di-dah
Y	dah-di-dah-dah
Z	dah-dah-di-dit

Foreign Letters

à, á, å	di-dah-dah-di-dah
ä	di-dah-di-dah
ç	dah-di-dah-di-dit
ch	dah-dah-dah-dah
è, é	di-di-dah-di-dit
ê	dah-di-di-dah-dit
ñ	dah-dah-di-dah-dah
ö	dah-dah-dah-dit
ü	di-di-dah-dah

Numerals

1	di-dah-dah-dah-dah
2	di-di-dah-dah-dah
3	di-di-di-dah-dah
4	di-di-di-di-dah
5	di-di-di-di-dit
6	dah-di-di-di-dit
7	dah-dah-di-di-dit
8	dah-dah-dah-di-dit
9	dah-dah-dah-dah-dit
Ø	dah-dah-dah-dah-dah

Spacing

A dash (dah) is equal to three dots (dit). The space between symbols forming the same letter equals one dot. The space between two letters equals three dots. The space between two words equals five dots.

Punctuation

Apostrophe	di-dah-dah-dah-dah-dit
Brackets (open)	dah-di-dah-dah-dit
Brackets (close)	dah-di-dah-dah-di-dah
Comma	dah-dah-di-di-dah-dah
Error	di-di-di-di-di-di-di-dit
Fraction bar	dah-di-di-dah-dit
Full stop	di-dah-di-dah-di-dah
Hyphen	dah-di-di-di-di-dah
Inverted commas	di-dah-di-di-dah-dit
Question mark	di-di-dah-dah-di-dit

Appendix 6

The International Q-Code

The International Q-Code provides a means by which telegraphy (CW) operators can ask questions and give answers in a simplified form. Not all of the codes are used by radio amateurs and this extract lists only the ones generally encountered. A code followed by a question mark is of course the question and the same code without the query is the answer. For instance, 'QRA?' means 'What is the name of your station?' and 'QRA John' gives the name of the operator. To conserve space, only the questions are listed.

QRA	What is the name of your station?
QRG	Will you tell me my exact frequency?
QRH	Does my frequency vary?
QRI	What is the tone of my transmission?
QRK	What is the intelligibility of my signals?
QRL	Are you busy? (Reply QRL means 'Yes, please do not interfere.')
QRM	Is there interference?
QRN	Are you troubled by static?
QRO	Shall I increase transmitter power?
QRP	Shall I decrease transmitter power?
QRQ	Shall I send faster?
QRS	Shall I send more slowly?
QRT	Shall I stop sending?
QRU	Have you anything for me?
QRV	Are you ready?
QRX	When will you call me again?
QRZ	Who is calling me?
QSA	What is the strength of my signals?
QSB	Are my signals fading?
QSD	Is my keying defective?
QSK	Can you hear me between your signals and can I break in?
QSL	Can you acknowledge receipt?
QSO	Can you communicate with . . . ?
QSP	Will you relay to . . . ?
QSX	Will you listen to . . . on . . . kHz?
QSY	Shall I change to another frequency?
QTH	What is your location?
QTR	What is the correct time?

Some of the above codes are also used for telephony transmissions and may have general application within the hobby. These are listed below.

QRA	Name of operator
QRG	Frequency
QRM	Interference (other than static)
QRN	Interference (static)
QRO	High power
QRP	Low power
QRT	Closing (or closed) down
QRV	Operating, active (*eg* G7AAA is QRV on 3670 kHz)
QRX	Stand by
QRZ	Please identify yourself
QSB	Fading
QSL	Confirm (QSL card = verification card)
QSO	Radio contact
QSP	Relay to . . .
QSY	Change frequency
QTH	Location

Abbreviations in Common usage (other than Q-Code)

/A	Alternative address	FM	Frequency modulation
AC	Alternating current	FONE	Telephony
AE	Aerial	FREQ	Frequency
AGC	Automatic Gain Control	GHz	GigaHertz
AGN	Again	GMT	Greenwich Mean Time
AM	Amateur	HF	High frequency
AM	Amplitude modulation	HI	Laughter
/AM	Aeronautical mobile	HW	How
ANL	Automatic noise limiter	Hz	Hertz
ANT	Antenna	ID	Identification
AR	End of transmission	IF	Intermediate frequency
ARRL	American Radio Relay League	IRC	International Reply Coupon
ATU	Automatic tuning unit	IS	Interval signal
BC	Broadcast/ broadcasting	ITU	International Telecommunications Union
BFO	Beat Frequency Oscillator	K	Invitation to transmit
BURO	QSL Bureau	kHz	KiloHertz
CB	Citizens' Band	LF	Low frequency
clg	Calling	LSB	Lower sideband
CONDX	Conditions	m.	Metres
CPY	Copy	/M	Mobile
CQ	General call	MHz	MegaHertz
CUAGN	See you again	/MM	Maritime mobile
CW	Morse telegraphy	MNI	Many
DC	Direct current	MUF	Maximum Usable Frequency
de	From		
dip.	Dipole	OM	Old man
dr	Dear	OT	Old Timer
DSB	Double sideband	/P	Portable
DX	Rare, long-distance	PSE	Please
DXCC	DX Century Club award	PX	Prefix
ES	And	R	Received
FB	Fine business	RAE	Radio Amateur Examination
FER	For		

RF	Radio frequency	UR	Your
RSGB	Radio Society of Great Britain	USB	Upper sideband
		UTC	Universal Time Coordinated
RST	Readability-strength-tone	VA	'End of work'
RTTY	Radio teletype	VHF	Very high frequency
RX	Receiver	VY	Very
SINPO	Strength-interference-noise-propagation-overall quality	w.	Watts
		wkd	Worked
		wkg	Working
SSB	Single sideband	WRTH	*World Radio TV Handbook*
SWL	Short wave listener		
SWLing	Short wave listening	WX	Weather
TEMP	Temperature	XYL	Wife
TNX	Thanks	YL	Young lady
TRX	Transceiver	55	Best success
TX	Transmitter	73	Best wishes
UHF	Ultra high frequency	88	Love and kisses

Appendix 8

Addresses of Short Wave Broadcasting Stations

This Appendix lists the postal addresses of a selection of broadcasting stations heard in Great Britain and Western Europe. The lists of countries are arranged alphabetically within continents. This information has been taken from the *World Radio TV Handbook* 1987 and is reproduced by kind permission of the publishers, Billboard Ltd.

Europe

Albania: Radiotelevisione Shqiptar (R. Tirana), Rruga Ismail Qemali, Tirana.
Austria: R. Austria International, A–1136 Vienna.
Belgium: Belgische Radio en Televisie (BRT), P.O. Box 26, B–1000 Brussels.
Bulgaria: Bulgarian Radio, Bul. Dragan Cankov 4, 1421 Sofia 21.
Czechoslovakia: Czechoslovak Radio, Praha 2, 12099 Vinohradska 12.
Denmark: Radio Denmark, Shortwave Dept, Radiohouse, DK–1999 Frederiksberg C.
Finland: Oy Yleisradio AB, P.O. Box 95, 00251 Helsinki.
France: Radio France Internationale, BP 9515, 75762 Paris Cédex 16.
German Democratic Republic: Radio Berlin International, DDR–1160 Berlin, Nalepastrasse 18–50.
German Federal Republic: Deutsche Welle, Raderberggürtel 50, P.O. Box 10 04 44, D–5000 Köln 1; Radio Free Europe/Radio Liberty Inc., Oettingenstrasse 67, 8000 Munich 22.
Greece: Hellenic Broadcasting Corp., P.O. Box 1, Aghia Paraskevi 60019, Athens.
Hungary: Radio Budapest, H–1800 Budapest.
Italy: RAI — Radiotelevisione Italiana, Viale Mazzini 14, 00195 Roma.
Luxembourg: Radio-Télé-Luxembourg, Villa Louvigny, Parc Municipal, Luxembourg-Ville. (UK listeners should write to Radio Luxembourg (London) Ltd, 38 Hertford Street, London W1Y 8BA.)
Monaco: Trans World Radio, BP 349, MC–98007, Monaco Cedex.
Netherlands: R. Nederland Wereldomroep, Postbus 222, 1200 JG Hilversum, The Nertherlands.
Norway: R. Norway International, N–0130, Oslo 1.
Poland: R. Polonia, All Niepodleglosci 75/77, Warszawa.
Portugal: Radiodifusão Portuguesa, Rua do Quelhas 21, 1200 Lisboa.
Romania: Radioteleviziunea Romana, Str. Nuferilor 60–62, 79756 Bucuresti.
Spain: Radio Exterior de España, Apartado 156.202 — 28080 Madrid.

Sweden: Radio Sweden International, S-105 10 Stockholm.
Switzerland: Swiss Radio International, CH-3000 Berne 15.
United Kingdom: BBC, Bush House, London.
USSR: R. Moscow, Moscow, USSR; R. Kiev, Radio Center, Kiev, Ukrainian SSR; R. Minsk, Ul. Krasnaya 4, Minsk 220807 Byelorussia, USSR; R. Tashkent, Khorezmskaya 49 Tashkent, Uzbek, USSR; R. Vilnius, Lietuvos Radijas, Konarskio 49 Vilnius, Lithuania.
Vatican State: Vatican Radio, Vatican City.
Yugoslavia: R. Yugoslavia, Hilandarska 2, 11000 Beograd.

Africa

Algeria: Radiodiffusion-Télévision Algerienne, 21 Blvd des Martyrs, Alger.
Angola: Radio Nacional de Angola, CP 1329, Luanda.
Benin: Office de Radiodiffusion et Télévision du Benin, BP 366, Cotonou.
Cameroon: R. Nationale du Cameroun, BP 281, Yaoundé.
Chad: Radiodiffusion Nationale Tchadienne, BP 892, N'djamena.
Egypt: Egyptian Radio & TV Union, P.O. Box 1186, Cairo.
Ghana: Ghana Broadcasting Corporation, P.O. Box 1633, Accra.
Guinea: Radiodiffusion Nationale, BP 391, Conakry.
Ivory Coast: Radiodiffusion-Télévision Ivoirienne, BP V191, Abidjano.
Kenya: Voice of Kenya, Box 30456, Nairobi.
Liberia: Radio ELBC, Liberian Broadcasting System, P.O. Box 594, Monrovia; Radio ELWA, Box 192, Monrovia.
Mauritania: Office de Radiodiffusion-Télévision Mauritanie (ORTM), BP 200, Nouakchott.
Morocco: Radiodiffusion-Télévision Marocaine, 1 Rue El Brihi, Rabat.
Niger: Office de Radiodiffusion-Télévision du Niger (ORTN), BP 361, Niamey.
Nigeria: Voice of Nigeria, PMB 12504, Ikoyi, Lagos.
Senegal: Office du Radiodiffusion-Télévision du Senegal, BP 1765 Dakar.
Seychelles: Far East Broadcasting Association (FEBA), Box 234, Mahé.
South Africa: Radio RSA — The Voice of South Africa, P.O. Box 4559, Johannesburg 2000.
Swaziland: Trans World Radio, P.O. Box 64, Manzini.
Tanzania: R. Tanzania, P.O. Box 9191, Dar es Salaam.
Zambia: Zambia Broadcasting Service, Broadcasting House, P.O. Box 50015, Lusaka.

Asia

Afghanistan: R. Afghanistan, P.O. Box 544, Kabul.
Bangladesh: P.O. Box 2204, Dhaka.
China: Radio Beijing, Beijing.
India: All India Radio, Directorate General, Akashvani Bhavan, Parliament Street, New Delhi 110001 (home services); All India Radio, Directorate of External Services, P.O. Box 500, New Delhi 110001 (overseas services).
Iran: Islamic Republic of Iran Broadcasting (IRIB), PO Box 3333, Tehran.
Iraq: Iraqi Broadcasting & TV Establishment, Salihiya, Baghdad.

Israel: Israel Broadcasting Authority, Overseas Services, P.O. Box 1082, Jerusalem.
Japan: Japan Broadcasting Corporation, 2-2-1 Jinnan, Shibuya-ku, Tokyo.
Jordan: Hashemite Kingdom Broadcasting Service, P.O. Box 909, Amman.
Korea: R. Pyongyang, Korean Central Broadcasting Station, Pyongyang, Democratic People's Republic of Korea; Radio Korea, 18 Yoido-dong, Yongdungp'o-gu, Seoul 150, Republic of Korea.
Kuwait: Kuwait Broadcasting Service, P.O. Box 397, 13004 SAFAT Kuwait.
Malaysia, West: Voice of Malaysia, P.O. Box 11272, Kuala Lumpur.
Mongolia: Ulan Bator Radio, C.P.O. Box 365, Ulan Bator.
Pakistan: Controller, Planning & Research, Broadcasting House, Constitution Avenue, Islamabad.
Philippines: R. Veritas Asia, P.O. Box 939, Manila; Far East Broadcasting Company, Box 1, Valenzuela, Metro-Manila.
Qatar: Qatar Broadcasting Service, P.O. Box 3939, Doha.
Saudi Arabia: Broadcasting Service of the Kingdom of Saudi Arabia, Ministry of Information, Riyadh.
Sri Lanka: Sri Lanka Broadcasting Corporation, P.O. Box 574, Torrington Square, Colombo 7; Trans World Radio, P.O. Box 364, Colombo; Deutsche Welle relay Trincomalee, 6 Queens Avenue, Colombo 3.
Syria: Syrian Broadcasting & Television Organisation, Place des Ommayades, Damascus.
Taiwan: Voice of Free China, 55 Pei An Rd, Ta Chih, Taipei 104.
Turkey: Turkish Radio-Television Corporation, K. 333, 06-443, Ankara.
United Arab Emirates: U.A.E. Radio & Television — Dubai, P.O. Box 1695, Dubai.
Vietnam: Voice of Vietnam, 58 Quan Su Street, Hanoi.

Oceania

Australia: Radio Australia, P.O. Box 428G, GPO Melbourne 3001.
Guam: Trans World Radio Pacific (Guam): Station KTWG, P.O. Box ED, Agana, Guam 96910; Station KTWR, P.O. Box CC, Agana, Guam 96910.
Indonesia: Voice of Indonesia, P.O. Box 157, Jakarta.
Marianas Is.: Far East Broadcasting Company, P.O. Box 209, Saipan.

North America

Canada: Radio Canada International, P.O. Box 6000, Montreal, Canada H3C 3A8.
Costa Rica: R. Reloj, Ap. 341, San José.
Cuba: R. Habana, Apartado 7026, La Habana.
Haiti: Radio Station 4VEH, BP1 Cap Haitien.
United Nations: United Nations, New York, N.Y. 10017.
USA: Voice of America, United States Information Agency, Washington DC, 20547; WYFR — Family Radio, 290 Hegenberger Road, Oakland, Calif., 94621; International Broadcasting Station KGEI, Friendship Station, Redwood City, CA 94065; Station WINB, P.O. Box 88, Red Lion, PA 17356; WRNO Worldwide, P.O. Box 100, New Orleans, LA 70181.

South America

Argentina: Servicio Oficial de Radiodifusion (SOR), Casilla de Correo 555, 1000 Buenos Aires.
Brazil: ZYF 278, R. Nacional Manaus, CP 2929, 69000 Manaus, AM; Radiobras network, CP 04/0340, 70323 Brasilia.
Chile: R. Nacional de Chile, Cas. 244-V, Santiago.
Colombia: R. Sutatenza, Ap. A 7170, Bogota, DE.
Ecuador: La Voz de los Andes (HCJB), Casilla 691, Quito.
Netherlands Antilles: Trans World Radio, Bonaire, Netherlands Antilles.
Venezuela: R. Nacional Caracas, Ap. 3979, Caracas 1010.

Appendix 9

DX Bulletins in English from Broadcasting Stations

This Appendix gives details of the transmission times of DX programmes in English from short wave broadcasting stations. The information has been taken from *World Radio TV Handbook 1987* and is reproduced by kind permission of the publishers. (Programmes in other languages are also included in *WRTH*.) Where the DX bulletin has a title or is part of another programme, the name of the programme is shown. Since the frequencies of transmission will vary seasonally they are not quoted. All times are in GMT.

Argentina: R.A.E. Wed. 1745; Thurs. 0100, 0400.
Australia: R. Australia. 'Talkback'. Sun. 0310, 0710, 0910, 1240, 1710, 2040.
Austria: R. Austria. 'Shortwave Panorama'. Sun. 0200, 0900, 1230, 1430, 1805; Mon. 0430.
Belgium: BRT. Sat. 1615, 1330; 1630; Sun. 0615, 1830, 2200; Mon. 0030.
Canada: R. Canada International. 'Shortwave Listeners' Digest'. Sat. 2115 (to Europe), 2137 (to Africa); Sun. 0108 (to USA), 2305 (to the Caribbean).
Czechoslovakia: R. Prague. Wed. 1915, 2145; Fri. 0145, 0345.
Ecuador: HCJB. 'DX Party Line'. Mon./Wed./Fri. 0930, 2130; Tues./Fri./Sun. 0230, 0630.
German Federal Republic: Deutsche Welle. 3rd Sat. of month, 0940, 1620.
Guam: KTWR. 'DX Listeners Log'. Sat. 0830, 1330.
Hungary: R. Budapest. Sun. 1700, 2100; Mon. 1700, 2100; Tues./Fri. 1515; Wed./Sat. 0400.
Israel: Sun. 2010, 2240.
Japan: R. Japan. 'DX Corner'. Sun. 2315.
Netherlands: R. Nederland. 'Media Network'. Thurs., 23 minutes after start of transmission.
Philippines: FEBC. 'DX Dial'. Mon. 0010; Tues. 1340; Sat. 0140, 2305.
Portugal: Adventist World Radio: Sun. 0915 on 9670 kHz; R. Portugal: 2nd Fri. 1800, 2030, repeated Sat. 0300, 0530.
Seychelles: FEBA. Sun. 0730.
South Africa: Radio RSA. 'DX Corner'. Sat. 2100; Sun. 0200, 0300, 0630; Thurs. 1300.
Spain: R. Exterior. Sun. 1915, 2015, 2245; Mon. 0045, 0145, 0545.
Sweden: R. Sweden. In all broadcasts from Tues. 1400 to Wed, 1230 inc.
Switzerland: Swiss Radio International. 'Swiss Shortwave Merry-go-round'. Sat., approx. 18 mins. after start of transmission.

Turkey: Voice of Turkey. Sat., fortnightly.
UK: BBC World Service. 'Waveguide'. Sun. 0750; Tues. 1115; Wed. 0430; Thurs. 0130.
USA: Voice of America: 'Worldwide SW Spectrum'. Tues. 1245, 1745; Wed. 0245; WRNO Worldwide: 'World of Radio'. Sat. 0400; Sun. 0030, 1400; KCBI International: Fri. 2030; Sun. 1830.

Appendix 10

Frequencies used by Selected International Broadcasting Stations

Major international broadcasting stations almost invariably use frequencies in the 6, 9, 11, 15 and 17 MHz bands and will often use other bands as well. In this Appendix readers will find a representative selection of stations with the frequencies, in kilohertz, used by them. Space does not permit the listing of all stations and the inclusion or non-inclusion of a particular station has no other significance. Radio Moscow and Radio Beijing (formerly Peking), which have a very large number of frequencies, could not be included as full details were not known at the time of writing.

Listeners wishing to hear the stations listed should check the frequencies shown but should not automatically assume that the transmission will actually come from the country giving its name to the programmes in those cases where stations have relay sites in other countries.

The information in this Appendix has been extracted from *World Radio TV Handbook 1987* and is reproduced by kind permission of the publishers, Billboard Inc.

AUSTRALIA (Radio Australia)

5995	7205	9645	11705	11855	15240	15395
6035	7215	9655	11720	11910	15320	15415
6060	7265	9710	11730	15140	15345	17715
6080	9505	9720	11765	15160	15365	17750
7120	9580	9760	11800	15180	15380	17795
7135	9620	9770	11835			

AUSTRIA (Radio Austria International)

5945	7115	9655	9725	11830	12015	15320
6000	7210	9660	9870	11840	15270	15410
6155	7245	9720	11660	11915		

BULGARIA (Radio Sofia)

6035	6115	7150	7280	9740	11765	11900
6045	6135	7155	9560	9755	11835	15310
6070	6160	7215	9595	11720	11860	15385
6085	7115	7255	9700	11735		

CANADA (Radio Canada International)

3925T	6065	7285S	9650	11840D	11945	15260
5960	6140	9535	9740D	11845	11955	15315S
5965D	6195	9555D	9755	11850	11960	15325
5995D	7155D	9590D	9760	11915S	15140	15390
6010D	7185D	9595T	11710	11935D	15150	17820
6015S	7230D	9615S	11720	11940	15235D	17875
6055T	7235D	9625	11775D			

The letters after the frequencies indicate the relay stations:
D = Daventry, England; S = Sines, Portugal; T = R. Tanpa, Tokyo, Japan.
All other QRGs are Sackville, Canada.

ECUADOR (La Voz de los Andes, HCJB)

3220	6130	9745	11740	11910	15160	15295
6050	6205	9765	11795	11925	15220	17790
6075	6230	9860	11835	11960	15250	17890
6080	9715	9870	11900	15115	15270	

FRANCE (Radio France Internationale)

3965	7120	9605	9860	11805	15180	15425
5950	7135	9715	11670	11845	15190	15435
5990	7145	9745	11690	11930	15195	15460
6040	7160	9790	11700	11955	15200	17620
6045	7235	9800	11705	11965	15300	17720
6055	7280	9805	11790	11995	15315	17850
6150	9535	9810	11800	15155	15365	21620
6175	9550					

Radio France Internationale has relay sites at Gabon and French Guiana.

GERMAN DEMOCRATIC REPUBLIC (Radio Berlin International)

5965	6115	7185	9645	11705	11890	15440
6010	6125	7260	9665	11750	15145	17705
6040	6165	7295	9730	11755	15170	17755
6070	7105	9560	9740	11785	15240	21465
6080	7115	9620	9770	11810	15255	21540
6105	7165					

GERMAN FEDERAL REPUBLIC (Deutsche Welle)

3995	6100	7150	9570	9735	11905	15405
5960	6120	7160	9585	9745	11915	15410
5990	6130	7175	9600	9750	11945	17715
5995	6140	7195	9605	9765	11950	17765
6000	6145	7200	9610	9770	15105	17780
6010	6155	7225	9615	11705	15120	17800
6020	6170	7235	9625	11750	15135	17810

GERMAN FEDERAL REPUBLIC (Deutsche Welle) continued

6025	6185	7265	9640	11765	15185	17815
6030	6190	7270	9645	11785	15205	17825
6035	7105	7275	9650	11795	15245	17845
6045	7110	7285	9670	11810	15275	17875
6045	7120	9505	9680	11820	15310	21540
6065	7130	9515	9690	11845	15320	21560
6075	7135	9545	9700	11850	15300	21650
6085	7145	9565	9715	11865	15355	21680

In addition to its transmitters in West Germany, Deutsche-Welle has relays at: Kigali, Rwanda; Sines, Portugal; Malta; Antigua; Montserrat; Trincomalee, Sri Lanka; and Canada. Some frequencies are used both in Germany and by the relay stations.

HUNGARY (Radio Budapest)

6025	7155	7220	9520	9835	12000	15220
6110	7165	7225	9585	11910	15160	17710

INDIA (All India Radio)

3295	7120	9545	9910	11830	15165	15387
3905	7140	9550	10335	11865	15175	17780
4860	7195	9610	11620	11895	15230	17785
6035	7215	9615	11715	11920	15280	17805
6105	7225	9630	11725	11940	15320	17830
6115	7255	9675	11730	15110	15335	17855
6155	7260	9730	11740	15120	15360	17875
6160	7412	9735	11810	15135	15365	
7110	9535	9755				

ITALY (Radiotelevisione Italiana)

5990	7275	9585	11790	15245	15385	21610
6050	7290	9630	11800	15310	17715	21615
6165	9560	9710	11810	15330	17780	21690
7235	9575	9780	11905			

JAPAN (Nippon Hoso Kyokai)

5965	6080	7180	9525	9695	11955	15350
5990	6120C	7210	9570M	9725	15195	17755
5995	7140	7280	9645M	11840	15230M	17785M
6065	7155	9505	9675	11875	15235	17810
6070						

Relay stations: S = Sines, Portugal; M = Moyabi, Gabon; C = Canada.

NETHERLANDS (Radio Nederland Wereldomroep)

5955	6165	9525	9715	11735	15315	21475
5990	7175	9540	9770	11740	15350	21480
6020	7230	9590	9775	11930	15560	21485
6040	7285	9610	9895	11935	15570	21540
6050	9505	9630	11710	13770	17575	21680
6110	9515	9650	11730	15280	17605	21685

Radio Nederland has relay stations at Bonaire, Netherlands Antilles; and Talata/Volonondry, Madagascar.

PAKISTAN (Radio Pakistan)

3980	7365	9505	11672	12005	15560	17620
4950	7375	9860	11735	12025	15565	17640
6175	9455	11615	11745	15115	15580	17660
6240	9460	11640	11790	15175	15595	17745
7315	9465	11660	11995	15515	15605	21475

SOUTH AFRICA (Radio RSA)

3230	6010	6160	9580	9615	15185	17780
4990	6065	7270	9585	11900	15220	21590
5980						

SPAIN (Radio Nacional de España)

6020	9360	9650	11715	11920	15365	17770
6125	9530	9675	11730	11940	15375	17845
7105	9570	9745	11815	15125	15380	17890
7275	9620	9765	11880	15215	15395	21575
7450	9630					

SWEDEN (Radio Sweden International)

6045	9565	9655	9715	11785	15245	15435
6065	9605	9665	9730	11925	15345	17770
7265	9615	9695	11705	11950	15390	21555
7275	9630	9700	11735	11955		

SWITZERLAND (Swiss Radio International)

3985	6165	9625	9730	11795	11935	12035
5965	6190	9665	9870	11840	11955	15430
6035	9535	9670	9885	11905	12030	15570
6135	9560	9725				

UNITED KINGDOM (British Broadcasting Corporation)

The frequencies below are used by transmitters in the United Kingdom and some are also used by relay stations in other countries. The BBC has relay facilities at: Berlin, West Germany; Ascension Island; Lesotho; Cyprus; Masirah Island, Oman; Singapore; Sackville, Canada; Delano, USA; Greenville, USA; and Antigua.

3955	6050	7105	7230	9575	11680	15390
3975	6060	7120	7235	9600	11780	17695
5965	6085	7125	7255	9610	11835	17705
5975	6100	7130	7260	9635	12040	17715
5990	6110	7150	7270	9660	12095	17790
5995	6125	7155	7320	9750	15070	17810
6000	6140	7170	7325	9760	15115	17855
6010	6150	7175	9410	9770	15180	18080
6015	6185	7185	9530	9825	15205	21640
6030	6195	7210	9565	9915	15235	21710
6045						

UNITED STATES OF AMERICA (Voice of America)

5995	9455	9630	11680	15185	15415	17810
6020	9465	9650	11715	15195	15580	17830
6040	9525	9670	11740	15205	17640	17865
6080	9530	9700	11760	15245	17710	21545
6125	9540	9775	11890	15265	17740	21560
6130	9550	9815	11895	15315	17765	21580
6140	9565	9840	11950	15400	17785	21590
6155	9575	11580	15135	15410	17800	21610
6190	9580					

The above frequencies are used by transmitters in the United States and some are also used by relay stations in other countries. The Voice of America has relay facilities at: Ascension Island; Antigua; Belize; Botswana; Sri Lanka; Costa Rica; Kavala, Greece: Monrovia, Liberia; Munich, West Germany; Philippines; Rhodes, Dodecanese Islands; Tangier, Morocco; Thailand; and Woofferton, England.

Index

Of further interest . . .

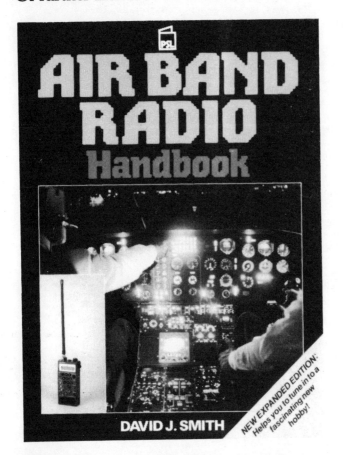

DAVID J. SMITH

Air Band Radio Handbook

With an air band radio you can eavesdrop on the conversations between aircraft and those on the ground who control them. This fascinating hobby, which is becoming increasingly popular, not only assists in the recognition of aircraft seen flying overhead but also provides an insight into the complex world of Air Traffic Control. David Smith, an Air Traffic Controller by profession, describes the types of air band radio available and their use. He also explains Air Traffic Control and its jargon so that you will be able to translate what you hear into what is actually going on above your head.